Testimony of Flight

Palewell Press

Testimony of Flight:
poetry and narratives

Jane Spiro

Testimony of Flight – poetry and narratives

First edition 2019 from Palewell Press,
www.palewellpress.co.uk

Printed and bound in the UK

ISBN 978-1-911587-17-0

The cover design is Copyright © 2019 Camilla Reeve
The front cover photo and all internal photos are
Copyright © 2019 Jane Spiro and were taken on location
The back cover photo of Jane Spiro is Copyright © 2019
Judith King

A CIP catalogue record for this title is available from the British Library.

ACKNOWLEDGEMENTS

The poems 'Wooden gods' and 'Leaving the Diaghilev family home' were published in the journal of the Oxford: Perm partnership January 2019.

The poem 'Playing for Time' was published in *Playing for Time* by Jane Spiro. (Oversteps Press, 2015).

The poem 'School Photo' was published in *Infinite Riches in a Small Place*, anthology of the Back Room Poets, and also, with 'Truancy,' 'Divided Heart' and 'Budapest Balcony', in *is a gateway* by Jane Spiro (Oversteps Press, 2018).

The Devon and Cornwall plays were performed at the Plymouth Museum concurrently with the Jews of Devon and Cornwall Exhibition. The scenarios are imagined from artefacts in the exhibition and also records in the Susser Archive https://www.jewishgen.org/jc.uk/susser/thesis/thesischaptertwopartone.htm

Factual information about Sara Coleridge derives from her own diaries and from the biography of Sarah Coleridge; as well as through my stay at Greta Hall, Keswick where they lived.
  • Memoirs and letters of Sara Coleridge: edited by Edith Coleridge (1875) https://archive.org/details/memoirlettersofs00coleuoft/page/n8
  • Jones, Kathleen (1997) A Passionate Sisterhood Palgrave Macmillan

The Vilna lines derive from songs found and translated from the Vilna ghetto.

Many of the Hungarian stories during occupation and during the Hungarian revolution derive from conversations with Judit Zerkowitz in Akadémia utca in Budapest.

The letters exchanged between the Polish girls and their brother and cousin Julek were translated from Polish and came from the archive of my uncle Julek Tigner.

Documents about changing name, naturalisation, and Sewek's letter from the Warsaw ghetto, came from my father's archive.

As a convention, text which has been 'found' is in italics. All the other texts are my own words.

DEDICATION

for the ones who took flight
and for those who could not

CONTENTS

ILLUSTRATIONS

PREFACE

This collection tells the stories of migration, leaving home and acclimatising to a new one, the irrevocable turning points, and the consequences which impact years later, and which enter lives subtly and without announcement.

In capturing these small moments, I am springing out from both historical moments known through documents and records; stories told to me by members of my family—my father who left Poland as a 16 year old on Kristallnacht, my uncle who travelled eastwards from Cracow to Vladivostok with a Japanese visa, my grandmother who travelled from Kovno and her sister who travelled in the opposite direction eastward; and the stories emerging from my conversations over many years with those who were migrants and survivors too from zones of strife, famine, revolution and war.

Each fragment is the development of a lived experience, my imaginative extrapolation from snatched stories or documents left behind; conversations: visits to iconic places such as gulag 36 in the Urals, the site of the Warsaw ghetto, a refugee camp on the Hungarian/Croatian border, or the square in Budapest that saw the birth of the 1956 revolution.

There are characters threaded through these texts, who have their own story and also speak for those who have been in flight for the same reasons and from the same place. They are composites of the stories of people who lived:

- Nadya: child of Russian dissidents smuggled to the countryside to be brought up by 'grandma', and then to the UK in 1938.
- Agnes: carried across the Hungarian border in the arms of her father, escaping from the Hungarian revolution in 1956, and eventually to Israel.

- Fabio: fled from Spain after fighting in the resistance movement against Franco, arriving in the UK in 1938.
- Reza: fled from Khomeini's Iran with his mother after the arrival of the Ayatollahs in 1979
- Turgay: escaped with his mother from Cyprus after his father died in the Turkish: Greek Cypriot war and the city of Nicosia became split in two, 1974.
- Motek: travelled from Warsaw in 1938 months before the declaration of war, with his parents Sol and Minka, leaving behind two aunts and a cousin. Sol's brother Bronich fled to Paris, later occupied also by Nazis.
- Julek and his friend Ludwik: travelled east from Cracow to Japan via Siberia, escaping Nazi occupation leaving behind sister Celine and cousin Irka.

I have also found myself travelling through time; and meeting characters who invited me to tell their story, such as the cast-aside wife of Samuel Taylor Coleridge, and the hopelessly jealous brother of Victor Hugo.

My message, in all of these, is that the specific is also the universal, and that the experience of one is the experience of many. Although many of the pieces are historic, returning as far back as the expulsion of the Jews from the United Kingdom in 1291, the currency of these episodes is left to the reader to deduce, and to consider our collective choice to repeat or to heal the messages of history.

The collection is offered as a series of fragments in whichever form suited the message: poem, story, prose piece, dialogues. Some of these are the actual found words of someone else and, if so, are in italics; but most entail my walking in the shoes of my character and generating the dialogue we were never able to have.

The fragments track a chronology of experience. The first section represents the world left behind: both the small daily events which made life pleasant, such as the games played in the wooden stedtl houses in the Russian steppes; or the 'push' which made life intolerable, such as the fear and the actuality of the gulag. The second section represents moments in the departure; the leaving of home and the journey away from home; the third section represents arrival and acculturation – both the moment of arrival, and the long-term consequences shown in small ways of what it was to live in a new culture with a family torn across continents. The final section records the connections with those left behind, the ties binding and fraying between those who made the journey to safety and those who did not.

Jane Spiro

PART ONE - HOW WE LIVED

Golden season, Pecs, Hungary

I

For all seasons this city
of cherries blushed and waxed
and primed in the sunshine of ripe vines
this Tettye of broken walls
and roads erupted in the rain

and this garden
where kittens prowl with jungle eyes
and figs swell
trees strip in the autumn dark
and the snow coats the squares
once brazen with tulips
and steaming with the fountain's summer tears

II

Of all time these villages
with paprika hung at the door
wells silted up with leaves
and rooves pitched like toys

children straggling to church in Sunday white
and old men with dialogues half finished
dozing after beer on benches
cart rattling by, horse shambling,
black as pitch to market

III

From the lake, children throwing
echoes and stones and whisking up
waves to frightened minnows
and sopping dogs
and winding by allotments,
picking the pickled plums
cherry jams and walnut palinkas of winter

Birthdays

6th birthday: 1951

She was a baby of the peace, born the year her father came out of his hiding place in the wall. Though she was born with scabs and protruding ribs from the starving months of her mother's gestation, she lived and became well and rosy. Most of all, she was supremely loved as the child born of a father alive against all the odds, and a mother who had been the face of normality while her loved one was hidden in the space between two walls.

Every year since coming out of hiding, her father took her out to tea on her birthday, just the two of them. Every year he celebrated this loved child, and the fact they could sit together at a table and that they could eat. The place he chose was the most favoured tea place in the city, over the bridge of the stone lions, up to the castle area above the wide sparkling Danube, and to the café where the cakes were a revelation and the sitting room with soft chairs was to be a countess from another age.

On her sixth birthday they walked together hand-in-hand and talked quietly and secretly about their lives. They walked, so absorbed in one another, they did not notice a man in a long coat standing in a doorway, quietly smoking. He flinched as they passed, turned his head to follow them as they walked, let his cigarette drop into the street. Then, as they turned the corner, he began running.

"Laci, Laci, is it you?"

Father turned, dropped Agnes's hand, then began to run also: "Oh Gyori, Gyori!"

Agnes stood at knee level, beside the weight of their coats, as to the two men embraced, and their voices came as if from the blood and muscle of them.

"You are alive! Oh, thanks to God, you are alive!" and Agnes learnt then that sometimes you wept because you were unhappy, but sometimes too, you wept because you were happy, and of the two, the latter was the more rare and the more devastating.

10th birthday: 1956

On this favourite of all days, Agnes and her father set out as usual to the birthday café, towards the square by the bridge. But this known place, whose every paving stone was familiar, had become something quite new. Here was a throng such as she had never before experienced consuming the square, and from the avenue another came flowing to meet them, the two merging and creating a human sea between her and the bridge. It seemed a great single animal had been born, one that chanted, that moved and there was a thrill in it, a cause she did not understand that made these people of all ages stand together.

It was only a heartbeat that changed it from ecstasy to fear, the time it took for a line of huge metallic tanks to roll forward from Akadémia utca on one side, and Vörösmarty Terr on the other, into the crowd. The young men who had shouted near to her, the women who had let her through and pushed her forward, scattered, breaking out into the side streets, and as they began to scream, it all turned to thunder.

Her father held her hand so tightly it hurt. Behind them the Russian soldiers were running with bayonets.

"Just walk," he said, "just walk as if you are not afraid, as if you have no reason to fear."

Though her father had been here before and hoped never to see it again, though Agnes had been the baby born into

9

peace and knew nothing different, though there was more reason to run at this moment than at any other in her whole life before or since, she bore up inside her the horror of the bayonets, the screams, and walked, slowly, step after step after step, her hand tightly, too tightly, held in his, and like this, through the dying streets, they walked back to their front door, they opened the door, they walked in, they walked up the stairs, they shut the door. Thank the lord, they shut the door, the outer one, the inner one, and yet again this place became a spot of sanity in a world imploding into darkness.

Budapest balcony

The balcony has always eavesdropped
on the street. When the people inside
were playing chess or attending to patients
or storing tins of beans against the hunger,

it poked its iron ear out into the street
and played the innocent with its pots of basil
and live shoots of thyme. But really
it heard how the coffee-shop rolled up
its metal blinds and enticed the early workers

rushing to their places of tedious repetition
in office buildings, neighbours learned of one another
as they met for the first time by the shared front door,
young men ran by to ply for peace in Freedom square
flying their flags with gutted hearts

and came back at night draped limp
over the shoulders of the living, the doctor
who lived in the upstairs room on the pavement
weeping, as soldiers paced by
with buttons shining like chocolate coins,

The balcony has always eavesdropped on the street,
its iron ear hearing all that passes,
playing the innocent with its pots of basil,
its live shoots of thyme.

1- Julek's door, 8 Sarego ulica, Cracow

Schoolboys

Julek - Cracow 1929

At school I was very popular: everyone knew me. They called me 'bashka' which meant 'barrel' as I was round and fat. We would play cards, or games with buttons. I was always with my classmates. We played in the Planty, which were gardens all the way round the city. Our class was very close-knit. Even now we know where every classmate is and what they are doing. Hebrew was obligatory, and also the tannach and Hebrew literature, as well as all the other subjects in the curriculum, even gymnastics which I was no good at. We started every day at 8.0 in the morning and home by 1.0 for lunch. I remember Schwerber, the music teacher, Landauer, the teacher of chemistry and physics, and a Mr. Waldeman. Although I was very average, by some miracle I passed matriculation with an excellent grade, but I never wanted to study. I was more interested in business and in my father's work in the fur trade.

Ludwik - Cracow 1929

Ludwik is the boy who does not like rules and who prefers to make them for himself. Ludwik is the boy who knows a great deal better than the teachers what the rules should be. For example, his teachers think stamp collections are a foolish waste of time and that history and Latin are more important. His teachers think that staying up till very late at night and then sleeping into the morning is very bad for a boy, whereas Ludwik knows that at these times his thinking is at its best, deeds can be done which are not seen, that darkness can be a boy's best friend and can save your life. When you are travelling or needing to survive from day to day on what you can find or on your wits, Ludwik is the boy you need.

Motek - Warsaw 1929

The work at school was easy for me. I would finish the task very quickly and wait, staring at the back of the heads of the children in the row in front, making shapes with my fingers on the desk. The teacher, Mr. Milosz, was irritated, I knew. One day, he came striding down the row of desks to mine and picked up my school notebook where the work was to be done. It was a mathematics task and easy for me, calculating multiplications which I knew by heart, and additions which I could do instantly in my head. The teacher held the book open at the page for today, ran his eye up and down my pencil calculations, flicked through the pages of the past lessons, and then without a word placed it down on my desk and strode back to the platform where he sat, underneath the blackboard.

The next day, I was summoned to see him in the teacher's room. I had never been in the room before, and only children who were sick or naughty ever went there. The room was smaller than I had imagined, full of papers and books and piles of school notebooks. But the biggest surprise was this: my mother was there too, and both of them looking at me most seriously and kindly, as if I was sick, and had not known.

"Motek, sit down. I want to tell you something. I thought you were a very lazy boy, not doing your work like all the others, idling your time instead. However, what I have seen is that the opposite is the case. You finish your work in half the time of the other children, and what you have done, as I see in your notebook is correct, and is presented with pride. In other words, Motek, and what I have told your mother, is not that you are the laziest boy in the class but that you are the most clever, and the class is too slow for you."

Then he was silent, and so was my mother, both of them looking at me. I didn't know if I should speak, or if so what it was I should say. I felt there would be consequences to such a statement, and I didn't altogether like consequences.

"I have suggested to your mother a plan, and I hope you will like it. Since you finish your work in half the time of the other children, you need something to give your mind an adventure. What the class does for you is not enough. What I propose are piano lessons. Mrs. Koppel is a very good teacher who lives two blocks from the school. You will start lessons with her tomorrow. When you finish your lessons early or when the class is too slow, you are permitted to practice the piano in the school hall."

Irka Koppel, the piano teacher

Though I didn't really need another pupil, I agreed for the sake of Mr. Milosz who I liked. The boy arrived after school the next day. He stood by the door, and I noticed very dark eyes that seemed to be straining, perhaps because his hair was long over his forehead or because he needed spectacles.

"You can come in," I said.

He came in, very shyly, and sat in the empty chair I patted beside the piano.

"Have you played a piano before?" I said. He shook his head.

"I will show you what it can do."

For this first encounter, I chose Schumann's *Kinderszenen*. I played the scenes, first one, then another, the child's tears, dreams and nightmares, playing and tantrums. The small boy beside me was so quiet I had to turn in my chair to check he was still there. He was indeed still there. He was sitting, entranced.

"Do you like it?" I said.

It took a few seconds for him to muster the power of speech.

"I love it," he said.

"You can try," I said, and stood up so we could exchange seats and he could sit at the piano where I had been.

Most children, at their first opportunity at the piano, love to bash it with all their force as if playing the piano is a fight. But with this boy, he laid his hands on the piano keys as if they were made of glass, and his fingers spread delicately from the white to the black notes, tapping the black notes with the end of his fingers as if knowing from the start their need of a gentler touch.

When he came for piano practice, he would so much forget the time that I moved the hands of the piano clock to

16

make his stay shorter. I felt a little bad about that, but I have twelve pupils now and need the time for myself too. I don't think it hurt him, playing ten minutes less than he thought. No, it made his thirst all the greater. It also made him want a watch of his own so he could count time for himself.

Playing for time

For bar-mitzvah the family clubbed together
to buy a piano, one of his own
to scale mazurkas, rondos, nocturnes,
the courts of Esterhazy, Polish drinking houses,
bordellos and ballrooms, revolutionary sonatas,
sunken cathedrals, songs without words.

It rocked from sea edge to edge,
bore its burden-voyage, jaws closed
in the damp ship bowels

to the cold north, new neighbours,
sealed doorways, languages
without words, unsung home.

Its voluptuous curves, shining smile,
banged against walls, outswept arms
clawed the bony bars of banisters,
punched at closed windows

and then, its hungry ivory gnashing at air,
was demoted to the street, shuffled out,
a failure to fit.

We learn not to long for
things, to forget them
since they forget us –

not to long for
places we once sang,
spread under our hands,
felled with hammers.

2 - 1929 School Photo, Warsaw

School photo

The Jewish school, Warsaw 1929

In the school photo, four rows of children,
boys in white shirts, smiling, smirking, grimacing,
the girls in their tunics with box necks,
neat white collars, preparing for their futures -

still-faced that minute in the lens eye, in between
the fidgeting, failing to sit up straight, pulling
faces, sticking out a tongue, trying to make
teacher laugh, and in the bottom row on the left

there he is, my young-boy father, his face sweet
with life as yet unspent, his dark eyes staring
intensely at the viewer, who knows him now
more than he knows himself - how the shy

half-smile, the straining forward towards the camera,
the black hair cut straight above his eyes,
hold the story of the flight to come, the healer
he is to be, the spouse, the father, not yet known.

The moment is held here, *click*, before all,
line by line, child by child, scatter
with playground shouts, tugs of war,
hide and seek, empty rooms.

Changing the law

I was once the mirror of you
and you the mirror of me
but now they've made us different –
your way of being born and mine,
your way of growing up and mine,
your way of breathing and mine,
your way of learning and mine,
your way of being a son, daughter and mine
your way of dreaming and mine,
your way of remembering and mine,
your way of making friends and mine,
your way of believing and mine –
I was once the mirror of you
and you the mirror of me
but now they've made us different.

I was once one whole
but now I am divided -
my English half from my Polish half,
my Litvak half from my Gateshead half,
my agnostic half from my believer half,
my caring half from my selfish half,
my clever half from my stupid half,
my right kidney from my left kidney,
my right hand from my left hand,
my left ventricle from my right ventricle –
I was once one whole
but now I am divided.

I was once the mirror of you
and you the mirror of me
but now they've made us different.

Shut out

When Motek went to school that day he was looking forward to watching the history teacher pacing up and down with his hands in his pockets, back and forward, counting how many dates he could mention between the wall on one side and the door into the playground on the other. He was looking forward to seeing Wilky who had just recently become his friend when they shared a pencil, passing it back and forward between them so fast they did their sums as quickly as children with one pencil each. He thought about them, as he walked to school with the satchel crossing his chest, weighing so heavily on his left shoulder it was making him lopsided. He looked at his shoes and liked the way he walked into his own shadow and couldn't hold it down, it slithered away from him under his foot like a snake. So early in the morning the lamps were still lit and most schoolboys would wait another half an hour before venturing out in the cold. Motek liked to get to school early and practice the piano before the school hall filled up with the shouts and scuffles of children pulling off their winter boots and finishing their spelling tests, scribbling on the back of their school bags, balanced on their knees. Today he was practicing a Chopin waltz and he sung it in his head and imagined his fingers at the start, how they seesawed back and forwards between next-door black and white notes.

When he reached the school, the caretaker was there walking round the side wall with his bunch of keys hanging from his belt.

"You can't come in today," he said, without looking up. Motek was sure he had misheard him, or perhaps he was talking to himself as he sometimes did. So he carried on, round the long grey stone wall, and let himself in through the side door into his empty classroom. He took off his heavy satchel and hung it over the chair, then his soft cap that pressed his hair down and kept his ears warm. He loved these quiet moments in the classroom before the rush of the day, when he could finish his homework, and play the piano in the empty hall. Sometimes too the teacher, Mr. Milosz, would come in and they would talk a little, both of them shyly, a little briskly, as if he were a whole class of children, not just one.

Today, like some of those days, Mr. Milosz opened the door looking rather distracted, his hair standing up a little 'en brosse' as if he had been running his hands through it. He sat at the top desk without speaking, spread out his books, then said,

"Motek, come here a moment. I need to speak to you."

Motek threaded through the rows of desks obediently, and stood in front of Mr. Milosz, slightly raised above him at a platform in front of the blackboard. It occurred to him he had never stood in this position before, and at this angle with Mr. Milosz looking down on him, it looked as if he had no chin at all.

"Motek, I am sorry to say this, it is not at all what I want to say, but it seems that there is a problem about you staying at school. I want you to know that the problem is not here with us – you are good boy and work hard. What I want you to do is to go home and ask your parents. Will you do that Motek? Will you go home and ask your parents why it is you can't stay at school?"

Motek's body reacted first, then his heart, and only then did his head understand what he had heard. His mouth became so dry he couldn't speak, his voice would come out as a squeak if he tried. His heart, which he knew well, (he often listened to its beating), seemed to have become a lump of rock dropping through his body into his shoes and pinning him there. Maybe this is what it would be to become a pillar of salt, he thought, maybe this was what it would be like to die.

"Put on your cap and coat, Motek. Here, I'll help you."

Mr. Milosz took his hand and walked with him through the rows of chairs to his desk. This had never happened before, never ever, that Mr. Milosz had walked to the back of the room like this, or called him Motek so gently.

On the street again, back in the biting morning frost, Motek couldn't bear the thought of seeing his friends pour through the front and side doors, Wilky giving him his usual friendly punch on the shoulder, see them all fill up the desks in the classroom, banging the lids open and shut as if nothing had happened. His feet were burning, wanting to run, run, run. So he turned left instead of right, ran on the crunchy frosted road, ran with his satchel banging against his chest and his cap forming a hot band of sweat round his head. The voice in his head told him not to cry but to think, but then he didn't know what to think except that he had done his spelling test and there was no-one now who cared. His run slowed to a walk, and his walk for a while to a trot, looking from left to right at what the world was like at 8.30 am on a schoolday. He had never seen it, never before seen what other people did while he was in school. Here was the cinema and outside a big placard on the street: Laurel and Hardy! Roll up! Roll up! The Flying Deuces!

His thinking voice said clearly, "Go on! Go in!" as his body said, "where am I? Where am I now?" Somehow, with his pocket money pennies he could cobble together the entrance fee and his feeling voice was saying "yes, yes" and softening a little the rock inside him.

"Shouldn't you be at school, young man," the woman behind the glass said, reaching for the coins he offered, his hands hot with the shock of it all.

"No school today," he mumbled.

He sat in the second row in the empty cinema, put his satchel on the next-door seat, waited in excitement as the flickering images appeared on screen. Oh, he loved it! He laughed till the tears ran down his face. He loved the fat man and the skinny man joining the Foreign Legion, falling over, tripping everyone up. He loved the funny hats they wore and the way they walked like stick men. He laughed so much he cried.

Walking home afterwards, he vowed he would not say a word to his parents, not do at all what Mr. Milosz had said because why should he? Why should he now do anything he was told? If he couldn't learn at school then grown-ups could never help him again. He would help himself, learn for himself, have his own secrets.

When he arrived home, he knew for sure that now the world had turned upside down, because his father was home, standing in the kitchen with his back turned away from the open door.

"Motek's home," his mother said. His father turned with a new, strange daytime face.

"Talk to the boy," he said, walking past him to the door, touching him on the shoulder as if he was a grown-up, firmly, seriously.

Mother waited for father to leave and the door to close, then she came up to Motek, put her arms around him and pulled him in close to her, squeezing him so tight he could smell new smells from her hair and collar.

"Motek, we are going away tonight. You must get ready, we are going on the train. You mustn't be sad."

"Where are we going to on the train?" he said.

"England, my darling. What a lucky boy to be going to another country across the sea."

"How will we go across the sea?"

"The train will take us to the sea, then we will go on the boat which will take us to England."

"How long will we be there? When are we coming back?"

"We don't know, Motcik. We just have to see. We just have to be brave, all of us. Will you promise to be brave?"

England! In the centre of his inside eye he imagined Laurel and Hardy with their funny hats and the way they were brave and funny, and how you could trip up and fall over and still be brave wearing a uniform like the others.

"Yes mum, I promise to be brave," he said.

Truancy

One day, not knowing why,
you were locked out of school,
found another thing to do –
daytime cinema, delicious truancy,
sitting in the dark in the back row
beside a satchel and a Polish grammar.

You did not know this was the limbo
of leaving, daytime darkness, a paring
of life to black and white, how it started
separations – the horse's pull
on the street carriage, the boy you sat beside
in the school photo.

Now you are in a
cocoon of camera dark, the director
in his box of light, the crackle
of figures flickering in and out of shadow,
the silent mime.

It divided the world
in two: that which had come to pass
and that which was still to come,
the reel of memory with its repeated moves,
remembered scenes clicking off and on,

and that last scene
when the lovers walk into the horizon
and you can only imagine.

Song of the Sarahs: mother and daughter

In 1823, when Samuel Taylor Coleridge moved to Highgate to be a live-in patient of his physician James Gilman, Sarah his wife was dependent on the kindness of others to provide her with a home. For many years she lived in the house of her brother-in-law Robert Southey where she brought up her daughter Sara; and when Sara married, moved to live with her in Hampstead where she stayed for the rest of her life.

Sarah

you, dearest child of us,
our caste and our broker
of peace.

I remember the child you were,
the heft of your head
cupped in the palm of my hand,
the lay of your lashes, your
ways of seeming cowled in sleep.

You have been the deep knowing of my life,
my young Sara, myself. You have been
the hope of flight when I was bound,
the place of sureness where nothing stayed.
Remember our homes together ----

Sara

I see the bridge I ran to meet
at the edge of the garden, and so small as I was
slid *plop* ten feet surprising as a stone

and yet, you know, I did not fear
as the river greeted me, even the sharp shock
of the stone bed as it came up to bruise me
and the sudden arms of the boy on the bridge,
wondering why it was his hair dripped like tears
as he lifted me to the bank.

Sarah

Should I laugh to remember that,
as he delivered you back shivering and cold,
at my gladness to have you back,
warming your cold fingers like butter by the fire,
holding you like a charm, wrapped in towels,
or should I weep at the fear of losing you.

Sara

You were one, mother, that chose to laugh.
We did then, didn't we, when the others
walked the hills and came back with broken shoes
and tales of mists and death,
we watched the hills from the window,
saw their shapes like three bears,
their changing in the day from yellow
to red to blue. From our window
we travelled, books were our journeys.

When our rooms were at the margins, we made
of ourselves a centre, language
was our country, and we were
its makers and guardians,
we were its pioneers.

Sarah

What it was to be your teacher
like a farmer whose land bursts to bear fruit.

Sara

Perhaps I have failed you...

Sarah

Never.
I would always think
young Sara is my pride, but for fear
of the hurt of hubris, would not say.
I did wrong not to say...

Sara

How little I need saying to be done,
when it is your doing that marks me.

Sarah

And now you, my Sara, give me a home.
Without yours I would have none now,
I would be lost in a carriage
going to and fro with no arriving.

Sara

My nesting in you, you
nesting in me, when all is done,
I give you back what you gave
and you give it me again.

Now we are but a walk from my father,
and it seems to me for all his absence to you,
there is a coming together,
you and him. It pleases me to see it.

Sarah

Why would I not forgive
when so little of us is left?
I still find what we loved.
It came so quietly, as if after death.

We did always have the moments
when love opened our wings and
he called me dear and darling.
Even when love had nothing to show
but its cold demon, when I had no reasons left,
not a single quickness that had not passed,
every remembrance scared out of life,
I still couldn't let go of the way love
cursed me. When I had given it all,
I still loved him and couldn't be free from it.

If it had never opened my wings
it would never have shackled me; if it had never
teased me with its hopes it would never have
harried me with its bonds.

But it did: it did arrive, and it became
the evil charm that led my days, and all I knew
was to follow. So I am absolved,
and he is, and we cannot help it.

Sara

How little I knew of this, how much I knew of it.
All at once I lived you both.

Sarah

Your eyes showed that, even when you were
hardly grown. We did not know
how it was you had learnt sadness,
how it came so soon.

Sara

I had in me always the thought of a father - but
when my father pushed me away, could not find
the wild child he wanted me to be,
was it I too tightly bound, or was it my dress?

Pulled to him and away, I never knew
which was right, why I was sad.
I thought I was sad because my dress did not please
because of wishes I could not understand or read

but now I wonder, in all this world,
of how much I am become him, how the wild child
is constant in me.

Sarah

I could not spare you from his absence

Sara

and I could not understand absence, how you learnt
to fill it, how it never left you.

Sarah

I remember as a girl how it was
I could be loved for my hair alone,
thick and strong as a horse's tail,
I would pull it and wrap it
like warm chocolate,
my banner of girlhood, my new world.

Sara

We think beauty will make our path smooth
but it comes to be our battle. My husband
is my love and yet I hold him away,
what he wants of my beauty feels at times like
theft, and I long to go where I can not
be found, can be found only by myself.

Mother, is that bad, is it as a wife should be?
Is it right, the running away that sits in me?
Am I as a wife should be?
Is it right, that as I stay I long to run away?

Sarah

All the ways we *should* be are other,
not ourselves. Never care for them.
I have heard of **should** from
every mouth that spoke
and not one was right.

I did not blame him when the smallest,
swollen and fevered in my arms, left
this world without his father's sight.

I did not blame him when I lost the hair
I wound around my neck like warm chocolate,
my grief scalped me, my sacrificial lamb.

I did not blame him that I made my home
in the house of aunts, the kindness of others.
I did not blame him that for all the words,

none fed the fire or made the broth. I did not blame
the friends who pumped him with self-love
made of us stones, and blights, and scolds.

I did not blame the poppy for becoming
his king, his owner, I knew it crept on him
by stealth, it claimed his soul.

I did not blame him for strumpetting
to all the world his other love, it shamed
but him, his struck and hopeless star

but I blame that forgiveness calms the past,
that time is content with lies, that in all this
noise, no-one heard that his story
was my story too.

Two sisters (two aunts)

One sister wants life without change,
the other wants to live each day anew.

One knows things are false or true
the other thinks life is full of middle grays.

One takes life quietly day by day,
the other sees it in bursts of dark and light.

One feels home is life's first delight,
the other loves the taste of the open road.

One sees family as the central node,
the other sees the world as helter-skelter.

One longs for home as gentle shelter,
the other the wild of the wide-flung sky.

Yet they are neither I nor she,
as both are her, and both are me.

Letters from Warsaw

The two sisters and their families were moved overnight into the same apartment. To do this, they had to not care about the walnut dresser, the gilt-framed mirror, the leather-bound editions of Tolstoy, the set of flowered Hungarian porcelain they left behind. It was essential not to care. There was no space now to spread their own combs and coats, to cook their own fried fish, to save up for Sewek's piano lessons, or for Lucia's ballet classes. They were thrown together into a kitchen that smelt of their skin and the damp clothes that had nowhere to dry, and the pans that without soap or hot water were never clean. The long bony chair in the second room doubled as a bed for the children, laid head to toe like sardines. Now every night Lucia asked, *mama, when can we go back to our real home?* And then when they were restlessly asleep, the mamas would lay mats on the floor and set down to sleep beside them, their husbands next door in the kitchen, sharing the last carefully saved cigarette, passing it between them like a talisman that gave them the past, until it collapsed into ash. In the kitchen they carried on a kind of learning for the children now they were forbidden to go to school; but Lucia was four and still learning to read, Sewek was 10 and at the stage when sitting at a table with girls was a torment – the sitting, the table, and the girls. But the sisters tried, drawing letters with stubs of coal on the floor, making landscapes on the table with upturned cups, and reciting poems they had learnt in school. The children, Sewek, Lucia and Dan the baby, were as good as it was possible to be. They knew the torment of staying in was far far less than the terror of going out. With their own eyes they had seen what happened, and it could happen for nothing: if they walked on the pavement and not in the road; if they chose a potato that was round and not one that was rotten; if they picked up an apple core that had rolled

36

into the gutter and tried to suck it for its last flesh; if they covered their yellow star with a coat. Though it was a cave, it was their own, and they were together, and they could be cosy if they tried, and at night there were still nursery rhymes.

Somehow Sewek had a joy in him. He liked to imagine what his cousins Motek and Harry were doing in England. Never once did he envy them; he even felt sorry for them because he had heard it rained all the time in England, and people said *pardon me* all the time for no reason. It wasn't that he wanted to be in England, as much as he wanted Motek and Harry to be with him, in Warsaw. He often sat at the kitchen table and begged for a piece of paper so he could write a letter. He was only allowed one piece of paper a week, so he had to write slowly without any crossings out and changes. Then mother would check the spelling, and write a line at the end: *Greetings and yours loving you, Henja*

Dear Uncle Monku,

Here we have not many things to do but it is alright. I wonder what Motek and Harry are doing. If they were here maybe we could go skating in the park. Is it true it rains a lot in England?

Sewek.

Sometimes the letters were never posted, because the journey to the postroom some days became hazardous, if there had been an incident or if new guards were posted who always liked to be extra vigilant. But sometimes the letters were posted, and best of all, sometimes a postboy came with a reply. When a letter came it was like his cousins had burst into the room with their fine-boned faces, their black hair cut like puddings over their eyes, their way of skipping upstairs missing out two steps at a time.

Dear Sewek,

We were happy to have a letter from you. Now it is warm even though it is winter, much warmer than winter in Poland. We sometimes even go outside without boots. We went to an exhibition and saw something you would like, a robot that does jobs for humans. The robot makes a clicking noise like an alarm when it comes near. We all laughed a lot. But then it does very useful things too, like picking up a piece of coal and putting it on the stove. Maybe one day we won't need to do any work at all and machines can do it all for us. Would you like to come to England and we could go to the exhibition together? It would be wonderful if you could come. There is a train from Warsaw all the way to the sea so tell us when you can catch it. We are waiting for you.

With love from your uncle Monku and from your cousins who say hello, Harry, Motek and Mikie.

Sewek liked the idea of the robot. He built his own robot with pins and wires on the kitchen table, until the baby Dan knocked it all down with one swipe of his little fist. Then he used the stub of coal to draw it on the wall, with eyes on stalks and hands like scissors. Lucia drew a hat on the robot, and gave it shoes with laces, and they played games guessing what jobs the robot could do for them.

Dear Uncle Monku,

I have received your letter from 24 Feb. 1940. You are writing that over there is quite warm. You are writing about machines and about a machine, a robot, which interested me a lot. That it takes water and coal and makes alarm, this is very interesting. You are asking, if I would like to see it. I would like to see it very much but at the moment I cannot come to you. Kind regards for Harry and Motek. We are waiting for your answer.

Sewek

This letter sits folded at the bottom of the box where it has lived for seventy years. It was the last letter Sewek wrote. Because of this it was kept for so long, like a memento from a secret love– a way of keeping a part of him, just a little part.

Songs from the Vilna ghetto

A composite derived from anonymous songs found and translated from the Vilna ghetto

Hey come and buy, come and buy!
Merchandise is going cheap today!
A life for a penny, a penny for a life!

We stand by the walls with hearts squashed
with arms hanging by our sides
as a weeping willow.

Hey, come and buy tobacco.
These days merchandise is going cheap as dirt–
a life for a penny, a penny's what I earn.

Spring has returned to the land,
golden now the beginning of autumn.
What does it matter, spring or autumn
when you see them with eyes tightly shut?

Who wanders on unfamiliar roads?
Who ventures a foot with courage?
Bring the youth out to meet them –
the elders too.

Youth is for anyone
who wills. We are all children
in the new free time to come.

Our song is brimmed with sadness,
       but our step is firm.
       Though the enemy guards the gates
       our youth will storm through with song.

Hinei matov oo manayim
Shevet ahim gam yahad.
       How good, how delightful it is
       for all to live together like brothers.

The Railway boy - Astapova station

Russia 1910

I began working on the railway when I was 12 and I had never seen anything like this before. I knew how to read and write, I had been taught early on playing cards with the night watchman, and I never forgot. It was useful. I never thought it would be but I could read the names of places on boxes when people arrived. They didn't very often, which is why this was unusual. They said the old man hadn't intended to stay but was taken ill on the train coming from Moscow. I saw him from the back as they helped him in to the railway shed, then only the top of his head above the sacking. He wasn't very comfortable; there was nowhere proper to lie there and he moaned and complained a lot but you would, wouldn't you, with all that noise around you.

I tried to do my job waiting for the train, opening and closing carriage doors and sometimes helping ladies with boxes, dragging them from the steps above the rail to the platform or the other way around, from the platform to the carriage. I never minded. It made the day more interesting and sometimes the bags were hatboxes and quite light to lift. But the usual were one or two a day and even that was always a bit of excitement. So I wasn't expecting this, and didn't have arms enough to do it all. Even if I'd grown ten more it would still have been no good. Usually I would exchange a few words and if I was lucky a few rubels, but not with this lot. They all arrived as if in a great hurry but to go nowhere, pushing each other, shouting over each other's heads, but who to I just don't know. Only this one lady, she seemed quite grand, she was portly like a bustling chicken, she stood on the steps outside the railway shed and wrung her hands, shouting and sobbing.

I ran up and down the platform hoping someone would hire me, there's lots I can do, and I can swim and climb trees too, and it occurred to me I could pick pockets easily, some of these people would have quite good watches and snuff boxes in their pockets, maybe made of gold. But then as easily in the crowd could I disappear well just as easily could I be picked up again as there seemed to be eyes everywhere and to be honest such a scrum of people you couldn't get away quickly. Some of the clothes were like city clothes, but some were rough like mine, you could work in the field with them with no trouble.

After all these days and weeks here, I was getting tired. Instead of all these people going away, they just wouldn't. In fact, they are filling up the platform. Some have set up their homes here. One of them tells me his name is Yasupov.

"I am not moving until it's all over," he says. Because he wears shoes tied to his feet with string, and his clothes hang too loose over his long bones I did not want to seem more stupid than him by asking what it all meant.

It really is as if the world has gone mad—when suddenly I hear this groan as if the whole station, all of us, the shed, the platform, have lifted up into the sky. I have never heard a groan like it, before or since; it was like the world was a huge animal and had just died. And the groan spread, the way night does, from the railway shed door out to the people on the steps and the platform and the encampment but it was one groan, like black.

Yasupov, beside me with his toes bare, with blackened nails spread on the dust, turned to me a face streaming with tears. "Leo Tolstoy is dead," he said, "God save us all."

"God save us all," I repeated.

I am not quite sure why. But the name Leo Tolstoy thrilled me and being here, on the station, something had happened and I had been part of it.

3- Wooden Gods in Perm State Museum, Russia

Wooden gods

Mary has the face of a Tartar hunter's wife
after bringing wood in for the fire

Joseph the face of a Sylva fisherman
who has stood many hours in long boots
hoping for carp or perch

Jesus the face of a kungur hunter
up all night stalking the forest
returning at dawn with the pelt of a bear.

Mary Magdalen has the face
of the fisherman's daughter
after carrying water in a barrel home from the well

St. Peter the face of the Tartar logger
who locked the logs together with hand-cut cogs
to make the walls of the hut.

The villagers are at home,
halfway between neighbour and holy trinity,
stamping their face on the gods, and the gods
stamped in theirs.

How we lived

First are the steps up to the porch
or small landing before the door,
covered for those that wait from what falls,
sleet, rain, snow, hard in your face.
Here is brief shelter until the door opens
into what warmth you can muster from the wood-lit stove.

The kitchen is preparing for the evening,
the table top is spun sideways
so the beans and turnips appear in the box below.

The cradle hangs from a ceiling hook, the baby
wrapped in shawls, her cheeks pink from cold
or warmth, or fever and we all take our turn
to sit on the bench beside her, to rock her,
sing to her *Malinka, malinka – little one,*
sleep little one.

Above the stove the wooden shelf is painted
with flights of birds, fantasy lions,
and it is there we climb at night to sleep,
up by the roof, on the hard floor.

In the porch of the neighbour's house
a long iron sledge waits, the snow
thawing on its rusty branches.
We will get through the night.
We will work, we will play.

4- Stedtl House, Kulikovo, Russia

How we played

We are in a circle
all holding a string that joins us,
our fingers circling it.
The one in the middle runs round the circle
and as he touches each set of fingers, we uncurl them
so quickly the string doesn't drop.
And we laugh and laugh clutching the string
as it falls
and the one in the middle goes pink and puffed
and tries to catch us out.

We are in a circle
each holding an upright stick
and at a signal
we all drop our stick and rush
to pick up the one on our left
before it falls
and we are rushing round and round to the left
laughing and grabbing and bumping into each other
and catching falling sticks
and growing warm with the running
our hair falling into our eyes.

Longing for the forest

You are squeezed to a crisp
by the pressing of bodies in a crowded bus
when the doors spring open
and two factory workers grey with labour,
a night shift care worker, a schoolteacher, three
all-night drinkers the morning after
squeeze into the space where you were breathing.

You might then go in your mind
to the place where you pick mushrooms,
light a log fire, wash from an icy bucket
pulled from the river, open the door
so the wood smoke goes out, the smell of damp leaves
comes in, and your dog

tears outside yowling with joy
like the bears there once were.

Stroking a bear

I did not expect to lay my hand on a bear.
Though we share a planet, the bear in his part
and I in mine, should our worlds collide
there can be no reconciliation.

Either we destroy you,
turn you to pelt,
baited and used as play

or you destroy us,
become your game, a morsel
hopeless in your claws.

Now I am awed by your stillness,
as we face each other, nose
to taxidermised nose, and I dare

to lay a hand on your marvellously thick,
richly brown, curled coat, covering
the strong brute bone of your back.

I do so with the utmost respect
and the utmost apology for what we
have done to you, and what you,

with nature's inexorable force,
have done to us – knowing
we should not meet like this,

I should never summon you like this
from the forest that is your domain,
know the strong texture of your coat

under my hand, how your fur coils
in spirals, anti-clockwise like the curls
on my own head, the head of my child.

Privilege

Gulag 36

The least privileged had a square of sky
cross-stitched with barbed wire
in the ceiling of a walking room, 6 paces
in each direction.

The next privileged had the chance of queuing
one by one to warm their hands
on a single stove giving out a radius of heat
the width of a small dinner plate,
a minor saint's halo.

The next privileged had the daytime chance
to haul timber twelve hours a day
come back to propaganda films in the red cinema,
a short shelf of acceptable reading.

But the most privileged had a row of trees
under whose shade they could bend
to pick white mushrooms, cook them in soup,
taste their warm muscle, imagine they were home.

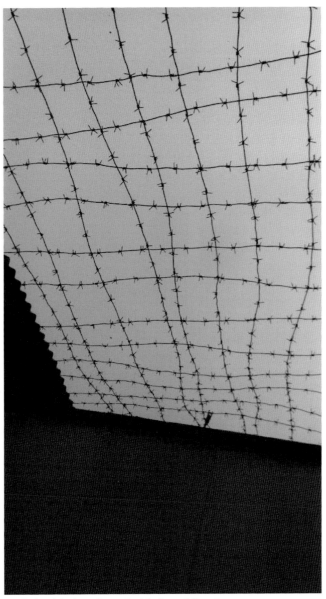

5- Gulag 36 view of exercise block roof, Russia

Kicking the wall

There were small things that made her sense something was different. Mama had packed her bag with the knitted rabbit who lived under her pillow; a whole bar of soap and her warmest vest even though it was summer. As she watched mama put them in her satchel, and buckle it up, she decided that if she refused to take the satchel with her then everything would be well again and the rabbit would stay in her bed where it belonged. So she screamed and stamped and scrunched up her shoulders so the bag wouldn't stay on. But mama became calmer and calmer in that cold steely way she did when she was angry and determined.

"Never mind, Nadya. If you don't want to carry these little things, which are not heavy and are only there to help you, then I will carry them to grandma's for you."

This day of playing with grandma was full of the unclear and unsafe and unsaid. Why did mama clutch her so strongly, and squeeze and squeeze and promise she would be back soon? These questions were not quite formed in Nadya's mind; they were more questions she felt in her blood. When she left quietly and closed the door, Nadya came to hate the back of the door and viscerally longed to break through it.

She lay down on the floor and kicked the door. She kicked and kicked, and screamed as she kicked, letting her shoes with buckles and hard heels thump the wooden panels at the base, thump, hate, bash, thump. It was the only thing to do with what she felt.

Grandma was standing at the side, waiting. Grandma had been standing there all this time, just next to her, saying nothing. She looked at grandma, and grandma at her.

"Have you finished now?" grandma said, very seriously as if what she had finished doing was useful.

I am tired of seeing the world upside down, Nadya thought, and rolled back onto her two feet. *You will always remember this,* said the ancient Nadya inside her, *you will always remember how it is when the door closes.*

6- Stedtl house, Kulikovo, Russia

Learning to sleep

Grandma had to carry not only her own sense of empty space, but those of little Nadya too. She could manage her own fears, only just; but Nadya's fears were so much harder to bear. Now they were in the dacha, in the woods where the dogs could yowl and leap freely. But how very very dark were the nights; and how desperate it was in the day, the scavenging for food, collecting wood for the fire, washing in the icy stream. For many nights Nadya had not slept, but stayed up waiting for mama to come back, standing at the open door, in case the light might lead her home.

Both of them, she and Nadya, were almost limp with lack of sleep, hallucinating during the day, diamond-awake at night. The only creatures that seemed capable of separating day and night were the dogs, whose days were wild and free, and whose nights were laid out by the last embers of the log fire, their noses twitching slightly. Sometimes one of their strong golden tails involuntarily lifted and dropped again, as if in dreamt contentment.

Nadya lay awake, like all these nights.

"Do you think mama and papa are asleep?" she asked grandma.

"I am sure they are," grandma replied, and hoped it was so, and that wherever they were, that gave them some hours of comfort.

"I don't know how to sleep," Nadya said in despair, "I don't know what to do."

Grandma looked at the two retrievers, lying with their legs stretched out on the warm flagstones.

"Look at them, Nadya, can you see? All around them is a cloud that carries them to sleep at night."

She laid the blanket on the floor between the stretched out limbs, and set the cushion for Nadya to lay her too-much-burdened head between theirs.

"There, you try," she said.

Nadya loved the dogs and to go with them to where they dreamed seemed like a heaven. She lay on the rough floor, pulled the blanket over her, and laid her head on the cushion. From there you could see the regular out-in of the dogs breathing, and without trying, her own breath began to slow down and follow the same rhythm. She imagined the sleep cloud that carried them away, and could feel it as a kind of cocoon of warmth between their two golden bodies. The warmth seemed to hum, very very quietly.

Grandma sat beside them for a while. Since Nadya's mama had pushed the handkerchief into her hand she had lost the layers that insulated her from the lives of others. Her son must have spent time unknown to her, embroidering the words with care and with dread. He must have carried it with him close to his body, in sleep, in secret, in readiness for any moment. He must have hoped for just a split second to drop it to the ground; and for just a single kind stranger to turn away from the scuffle and scraping of feet, pick up the ball of grey apparently randomly dropped, read the words stitched in so neither rain nor snow could damage it:

If you find this please take to my wife 62 Chaykovskaya ulica. I have been taken.

Since then she lived through his imagined hours of penance for being alive at this time and in this place. Since then she lived only to serve, child, grandchild. Her joys were small; please give Nadya the comfort of sleep, for just one night.

One dog let out a long, contented fart. Nadya's nose wrinkled in her sleep, curled between them, all three breathing in out, in out, and it was just for a moment as if the world were kind again.

PART TWO – LEAVING HOME

Leaving

Leaving is a monster,
devouring in small morsels.

it devoured my friends that prayed and danced,
the seller of fish, the maker of sweets, the mender of clothes,
the grid of our streets, the times of bustle,
the times when night was a time for sleep.

Love did not save them, nor tears,
nor shouting to the monster as it roared.
Leaving has devoured them
and left of them nothing that can be saved.

The monster of leaving has stolen our breath,
left a past we try to remember,
a future that can never be grasped.

Now I have left once, I will always be leaving,
will never finish saying goodbye.

Leaving dresses

I leave the dresses hanging still on their rails.
There they are, cutting an emptied dash.
They are everyone now,
cutout women

a silken ghost
floated in from a body I once wore.

This dress clothed a soul -
satin for secrets,
pearls for circling the world,
velvet for wearing the night.

I leave the dresses hanging
                                        emptied
cutout
                    and I
like a ghost
                            wearing the night

Last day in the Diaghilev house:

Perm, Russia 1919

On this last day they made a picture of each room
to remember how it was:

the salon
with its upright chairs
like the braced backs of dancers,
dressed in the yellow and lilac of firebirds:
that long lovely swathe of wooden floor;

the dining room
with its white cloth
laid with gold-rimmed bowls and plates
awaiting soup, ready for the talk, laughter,
best cut of beef, red wine of the next day -

held in monochrome memory,
a still life before the change of cloth,
handing over keys, laying them out on the tray
like the limp limbs of a sacrificial bird.

7- Diaghilev House, Perm, Russia

Closing the door

She is dressed in felt black hat with wide brim and best winter coat buttoned to the neck for last warmth. She knows the leaving is for a greater good, for some greater cause, but she has forgotten what it is, or who believes in it. She turns woodenly at the closed door, walks out to the street as if someone may see her thoughts from the lay of her hat or the stiffness of her walk. If she looks back, she will be struck down; not by others, but by her own resistance and that is the struggle. The struggle is who she belongs to, and now, where she belongs. Everything she needs for living, everything she remembers about it, is behind the closed door, yet she is on this side, and all of that, to the very last mothball, is on the other side and who knows if they will ever again come together.

Julek's journey - Poland 1939

At 7.0pm the roads filled with horses, bicycles, cars. We just followed everyone else, walking in the same direction as them. We ate our first breakfast in a turnip field. We found water, and drank and ate. Then we carried on east towards Rzesznow, arriving in daylight. Rumours started that the Germans would occupy within two hours. So we packed our rucksacks and carried on walking. We didn't reach the next big town, Przemilismy, until nightfall. A shopkeeper's family let us stay with her. There was no room in the house, so we slept in the shop on the counter. We all slept that night on the shop counter. People had said that Jews were rich, but they lived in poor wooden huts just the same as everyone else. Every home that welcomed us was Jewish.

During the night our landlady woke us up to say, the Germans are an hour away. She gave us bread and milk. I wanted to give her a handful of zlotys.

"No, no," she said, "all I want is that, when you are safe and have made a success of your life, if you survive, you give it to someone who needs it."

Walking eastwards through Przemysl at about 8.0 in the morning, we saw an old woman carrying a hay stack on her back. Suddenly she threw it down and started running. We ran after her. We didn't know what was happening, but we just followed everyone else. They were all rushing towards the vodka warehouse. We discovered the Polish authorities wanted to clear the warehouses before the Germans occupied. Vodka was worth millions, it was worth more than money. It was like gold dust. Within minutes we could be millionaires because you could buy anything you wanted for vodka. We took as much as we could carry, putting it in our rucksacks, pockets, anywhere we could hide it.

Oszmiana was a tiny village I had never heard of before. It was within walking distance of the Russian border, and the poorest village I had ever seen. In this poorest village I found the poorest family. They lived in a small wooden hut with a mud floor that got wet when it rained. They gave me a blanket and let me sleep on the floor. On Friday morning I went to the market and bought a chicken for the woman of the house. She used every single scrap of the chicken, even the feet and the gristle. Not one part was wasted. That chicken was like a whole banquet for them.

After leaving the village, we began to go east. It was evening and already getting dark. The roads were filled with horses, bicycles, cars and hundreds of people on foot. It was chaos. We didn't know exactly where to go, but we just followed the others, walking in the same direction as them. We walked all night in the starlight on the roads, meeting hundreds of other men also walking east. We went towards Wieliczka, the salt mines. I remember there was a grand house with big grounds on the way, and of course we wanted to see if we could sleep there for a few hours as it was getting very late. The door was slammed in our faces and we were told to leave. As we left, they put a sign up outside the door saying, "No room, don't disturb, go away." Poor people in houses offered food, rich people closed their doors.

Motek's journey - Poland 1938

Minka and Sol were sitting on opposite ends of the cart, with several large boxes labelled *Baltic Queen* in between them. Motcik had chosen to sit with Minka because he liked playing with her rings. They looked like toffees and he wound them round and round her fingers until she slapped him. Then he shuffled up and sat by Sol. Sol was sitting bolt upright with his hand out steadying one of the boxes. Throughout the whole journey, he sat there, with his hand on the B of Baltic Queen.

"Why's your hand out like that?" Motek asked.

Sol replied from the side of his mouth, so he did not need to turn his head.

"This mustn't move," he said.

But it was moving. They were all moving, and nothing could stop them now.

Motek strained his neck round to watch the wheels over the edge of the cart. When they went fast, the cobbles streaked into a hundred colours, pulling Motek into it head first.

Minka and Sol sat so they could not see one another, even at every corner of their eyes. One of the things you did, when leaving home forever, was not to look. Motek knew that. He looked at the cobbles and the wheels, because if he raised his head, even a fraction, something else happened. You saw the street hurrying in the opposite direction, running away as if with soft shoes, and knew you could hold none of it any longer, nor ever would again.

"Stop fidgeting," said Minka.

"I have."

"That's good then, that you have."

He thought he would use the sitting quietly to think good thoughts about England. He knew English. He had learnt the words he needed from Piotr who had learnt the words from

67

an Englishman who used to drink coffee in their street. The words you needed were:

Thankyou

A cuppov tea

I beggy pardon

The Englishman who drank coffee said you would be fine in England with those words.

Motek had packed carefully for the things he would need in England.

Wielhorski's piano sonata in D signed by the composer, to impress other children and help him make friends, a black marble, to play with the friends once he had found them, a black velvet suit with a white collar he could wear when the friends invited him to tea, and also if the King ever came to tea.

Motek tried to remember good things about England, but that was difficult as he didn't know England. When he imagined England, he saw a King with a large cup of tea sitting on a white rock called Dover.

Motek was thinking these things very hard, sometimes with his eyes closed, when he felt something change in the light and he twisted round again to look. For a moment, a split heart-second, he felt like he was going on a wonderful holiday, because the purple sea had appeared, and a swan wafted by on the edge of the sea like an electric-blue ghost. Minka was looking at him, and her face had begun to move out of its mother-mask of control.

"Look where we are, Motcik," she said.

"Yes," Motek said, because he was looking.

"It is so beautiful here."

"It is" he said. It was the Baltic.

It was the Baltic, like the page in your favourite picture book.

Then it began, the city, the sooty suburbs, and then you couldn't stop time anymore because it came rushing up to you with the smell of the docks, the clang of steel and stink of diesel, oily plaits of rope, throngs of people with white faces and tattooed arms and then Motek, whose leaving had been a thing in his head, had not known how big it was to leave: but now the leaving filled the whole night sky with a huge wall of lights and windows. The Baltic Queen. The great Queen that devoured whole wooden boxes, and people like small morsels.

Sol climbed out from the other side of the boxes and the carter climbed out and there was creaking and wrenching as the boxes were lifted over the dropped rail of the cart and onto the shoulders of porters. Sol was paying the carter and the carter was embracing him.

"Goodbye Mr. Elderkind," the carter was saying, "goodbye."

He was beginning to weep, the carter, saying "Mr. Elderkind" again, then again. In that moment, Motek understood something. There are so many things; your friend who sat beside you in the school photo, your cousin Sewek with black eyes, the man selling fish you had never spoken to, the chunder of the tram, the big door of the piano school, the girl doing singing practice behind the closed door. But whether they were big or small, and no matter how much you loved them, they were slipping away. They were all slipping away.

We came in boats - Land's End 1200 AD

We came in boats.
We landed in your country.
It was the land's end
>the rocks and seals
>the mackerel washing in to the shore
the long coming-down of the sun.
And we called the place
Ruth Ketzei Ha Eretz.
Land's End.

Synod by royal edict his Majesty Edward 1st July 1281
- *All Jews are forbidden to hold office of any kind, or for any Gentile to facilitate the holding of that office.*

Synod of Exeter under the jurisdiction of Peter Quivil 1287
- *No Christian shall take medicine from a Jewish doctor.*
- *Jews must pay taxes to parish clergy and wear a distinguishing badge when out of the streets.*
- *They are forbidden to appear on the streets or have their windows open at Easter.*
- *Jews and Christians are not to visit each other or join in any festivities.*
- *They are not to enter churches or build new synagogues.*

By order of the King, Edward 1st July 18th 1290
- *To the sheriff of all counties in England:*
- *All Jews are ordered, on pain of death, to leave the realm before 1st November 1290.*

Do not ask for us on the rocks of Halagon,
or at the bridge at Bovey where once we passed.
On pain of death we pass no more
and you will not hear us
      you will not hear us
          no, now we are quiet
              you will not hear us.

Do not ask for us
on the Lizards, on the black moors
on the sands at Porthminster
in the streets of St. Ives, the Falmouth lanes.
    We are not there.

The trial of Johanna

Based on the case of Johanna of Dartmouth 1291

Prosecutor: Is it the case that you entered the port of Dartmouth and did so without reference to the royal edict of our sovereign Edward 1?

Johanna: It is not true.

Prosecutor: I am given to understand it is true.

Johanna: We entered the port of Dartmouth in order to earn an honest living.

Prosecutor: It is not your right to earn an honest living.

Johanna: Not a right to earn an honest living? Then is it a right to earn a dishonest one?

Prosecutor: You jest, madam. You understand well my meaning. You are a Jewess.

Johanna: Then if am not to earn an honest living, I will earn a dishonest one to please the realm.

Prosecutor: It is of no concern to me, nor to the kingdom of England or to our sovereign Lord. Our concern is that you take yourself elsewhere and absent yourself from this place immediately and as from this moment on pain of death.

Johanna: I am willing to live by the laws of this land and as a citizen of this land.

Prosecutor: To do so you must be other than who you are. As for who you are, such a thing is not nor cannot ever be possible.

Johanna: I am a mother and a seamstress. Are mothers not allowed in this realm? Is this realm to breed a regiment of monsters without mothers? Then I pity it.

Prosecutor: You are perverse, madam. Mothers we have in plenty. It is not that part of you the realm denies. That is a matter of your own body. It is your faith that concerns us.

Secretary to the court: (whispered) I understand there is a principle of conversion, sir. They can be admitted as converts to the Christian faith. I've heard it done sir. They've done it, the vicar of Buckfastleigh, he done it sir.

Prosecutor: Done by royal edict?

Secretary to the court: By royal command to the Keeper of the Domus Conversum. This bit here sir.

Prosecutor: *I decree that converts who intimate in good faith conversion to the Christian faith be admitted for the term of their lives to the sovereignty of England and grant them the wages of the converts, 1 penny per day.* Are you able to satisfy us in this matter madam?

Johanna: To convert?

Prosecutor: To convert.

Johanna: And for this you will have mercy on my life?

Prosecutor: The realm has mercy, by the decree of the king Edward 1 whose servant I am.

Johanna: This act will give me the freedom to be a mother and earn an honest living in the port of Dartmouth?

Prosecutor: Provided that you submit yourself to the good faith of this realm.

Johanna: My God has no doubt of this. He says *you* are the one that must act in good faith.

Prosecutor: Your God? In this case, and by your submission, your God is now our God.

Johanna; Exactly so. This was always the case.

Prosecutor: You are droll, madam. Have you accepted our conditions?

Johanna: Indeed my change was so swift you hardly saw it. My God has become yours with such alacrity you did not see him change.

Prosecutor: Indeed I did not. God alone looks into your heart but we as men on earth look to your words and to the vows you will make before the Lord. Release her. She is a freewoman of our town. In faith, she worships our God.

Johanna: And you worship mine.

The story of Moses Leib

He was a fine man
a silk merchant, travelled by horse and cart, horse by the
name of Zsusza. A fine man.
From Vilna he was, always travelling.
No family, he worked all the hours God gave.
Then one day
one day he's in the forest. It was winter,
white, snow everywhere, hard for the horse,
the cart piled high, rolls of silk, from China, Tashkent,
Samarkand.
Years it had taken to fill such a cart,
Zsusza, his only friend,
a horse, and a cart, all his life on the cart,
when suddenly he hears a crack
under the wheels of the cart
under the legs of his Zsusza he hears a crack
and he sees her hoof fall into a dark hole of ice.
A dark hole, it fell, and he must have had hardly a second
to understand
that his whole world, his horse and cart and silk, were falling
all together and him
into the black hole.
Oh he must have had a terrible shock
and to think that, after that, he had nothing left, he had not
a zloty, not a friend.

And then what?

He goes to Penzance in England.
How he got there I don't know but get there most
                              certainly he did.

And then?

He learnt the clock-making trade by watching and using
                              his hands and his eyes,
made the best clocks in the west, taught the young, gave
work to others, built a home, married a wife, joined the
community council, brought up four children.

The hole in the ice did him a good turn.

Did him a good turn, it did, though what a shock it must
have done him, and I wonder he ever got over it. But he did,
indeed he did.

The train

In the train the men have drunk their boredom as nothing changes in the landscape, and nothing changes in what there is to do unless of their own making. They are sitting in the dining car and there is beer, so they drink their first beer noisily and with relief to lose some of the minutes of those trees through the window, endlessly for hours, days. With each beer the waitress becomes more desirable, and their faces redder and their roars '*Kuku*' ruder and each of them in their head become emperors and valentinos. The waitress seems to accept that she is part of the delivery, the glass with its urine-lit liquor, gives in to the scrabbling for her lips and breasts, resists only when the glass is still in her hand and may spill, a short scuffle amongst their arms and her hair and their gristly chins, then back to the bar as the next customer waits for a plate of potatoes and mushrooms with onions.

Ludwik's journey

Though I had money for the train to Vladivostok I had no valid passport, so they refused me a Japanese visa. In the end I travelled to Vladivostok without a visa. I spent eleven days on the train. On the train there was a conductor who said, "I'll give you food and drink for eleven days if you give me your watch." So that's what we did. He had my watch which my father had before me and which I did not miss. I had caviar and vodka for the whole journey, brought each day by the conductor. I didn't like the taste of caviar at first, but by Vladivostok I had begun to like the taste. I didn't like the vodka at all and never came to like it.

The stations

The stations are a great excitement. They are a moment of hope because something has changed. There is a building with a name and the name is place, and a place is something and not the acres, the kilo-acres of the same. There is an arrow on the station nameplate. The arrow goes in one direction, so it is a limiting; I am going east, and there is no other way to go. At the station, there is the excitement of new arrivals to the train who are saying: yes, we know east is the only way, but that is the one we are choosing. They climb on the train with their cases, rucksacks. Those left on the platform are making faces at them through the window, miming the scribbling of letters and dialing of phones, mouthing I love you and kiss-kiss. But the east is a long long one-way direction and the train is sure of its direction and sure of its hulk of steel as it gathers speed knowing it is unstoppable.

Julek's journey

The journey took us through the whole of Russia. The train was always packed, with people hanging on to it and jumping on from the ditches. We played cards all the way. Deep into eastern Russia, in the middle of nowhere, we passed a small Jewish state they had created by a lake called Balka, Birobidjan. The idea was that all Jews would be repatriated here. I was curious, so I got off the train when it stopped there. At the station there was only one man taking tickets in a wooden hut with nothing to do; and an old lady with a stick who looked about a hundred years old. She blessed me, and I got back onto the train.

8- Trans-Siberian railway, Kirov Station, Russia

PART THREE – HOW WE ARRIVED

Souvenir exchange

The man on the train with the rumpled face and strawberry nose looks like a pastry cook with big forearms bursting from his black great coat and hair in disarray sprouting at a perpendicular from above his ears and cheeks that look warmly flushed from the hot oven. But in fact he is a philosopher travelling home from the bookshops of Vienna and Brussels with a caseload of books in German, Dutch, French and Greek on the life of Jesus, bought from the *pequinista* for a few francs here and there, or found under piles of books in the reserves of libraries or the repossessed homes of deceased aristocrats and purchased as a job lot.

Also in the carriage is a retired missionary nurse just returned from service in the Congo where she tried to keep the wards clean of typhus and teach the women to boil the cholera out of the water and believe in the word of God. In her suitcase is memorabilia of the baby Ignatia she had adopted but had to leave behind, Ignatia's christening cap and mug brought by hand on a two week journey by truck and mule, three ebony models of rowing boats, a family of elephants, the Bible signed with the names of all the other nurses as a tribute to her, and some of the ash from the clothes she had to burn when she caught TB, in a sealed box made of papier-mâché. The philosopher looks at her and marvels that a lady can be so out of touch with the day, wearing the kind of coat his mother might have shunned, and looking certainly far too big for her as if she had shrunk since first she believed it fitted her. She looks at the philosopher and wonders why a pastry cook should be taking the long-distance train from Vienna to Paris when the pastry was so splendid in Vienna, by all accounts.

When the train arrives in Paris, overcome by its familiarity when she herself felt so changed, she lifts the black suitcase nearest to the door and makes her way along the corridor; and the philosopher lifts out the neighbouring black suitcase, enough detached from the fixedness of things not to worry about its slight difference in weight and shape. And so they make their way, so that at night alone with the cased souvenirs of their past, she will find the heretic life of Jesus in four languages, and he will find a family of soapstone elephants, and both will wonder at the way things are, and sometimes at the way things are not.

Two brothers – Paris, 1830

Eugene Hugo, the second boy, brother of Victor

Eugene had one burden in life he could never escape, and yet he tried by every means in his power to do so. He was a poet who honed his lines by candlelight nightly, drawing all the burning pain of his spurned love and crafting it with the tropes and shapes of his classical learning into coiffured rhymes and heartfelt enjambment. Yet it was not quite as good as ----- he was always the one not quite as talented as ----- it was a shame he had chosen the same craft as -----. And he loved Adèle with the laughing black eyes, the lightness of her soul as she glided across the room in her small soft shoes and the way her smile opened up his hurt heart like a flower fed by light thinking he was the one ----- but how cruelly had he misread the love that was simply her natural alignment with the world, her natural state of grace – had he been a butterfly flown in under the open window and breaking against the pane she would have pitied him the same; had he flung himself against her in passing like blossom falling from a tree in the square outside, she would have brushed him away with the same firm delicacy. Such a shame he loved the same one as -----, longed for, pined for, died for, the same one as ----- lived as a chimera, a ghost, a shadow of ----- and let him, so much more worthy and blessed, let him live instead of ----- take my place, take my life instead of ------.

Portrait of Adèle Hugo – Paris 1837

She was the dark-eyed beauty two brothers loved. The shy light-curled one loved her with a kind of wide-eyed pain like a child torn too early from a mother, would follow her as she moved, knowing his eyes would scan her from the edge of her shoe to the curl fallen over her brow, and noticed when she flushed as she laughed, or went pale with news that troubled her. This love was too cloying and made her feel trapped by his gaze, out of breath with his attention, afraid to laugh as if the shape he had made her in would shatter. Then there was the genius, the one who seemed to have lived in the world many times, his look was knowing as if there were nowhere she could go where he could not follow, yet aloof as he chose in this containment not to follow. It was as if his grace gave her life, his all-seeing eyes made her representative of his world, and she became in him both she entirely and not-she but all women that suffer and love and search for meaning. She was through him just a mite on the face of the planet, and a goddess containing all: how his genius made her this. She believed she loved him and made the marriage vows fervently as if every word laid down their future.

So it was the more bitter now the brother had died of grief, alone and believing himself unloved, and the one she married had turned his light to another love that she knew was deeper than theirs had ever been. It seemed to course through his whole self and lighten everything he touched. She knew him too well after all these years not to see that she had become the arrangement of furniture to him, the expected shape of the day, whilst this new woman gave him shafts of vision and made him laugh with a kind of wildness and brightness that hurt her in its vulnerability. This new woman sat between them always, whether she was there or not, for there was not a moment when the wife was more visible to him than the absent woman he really loved.

So she poses for the painting in her best cream dress and knows her beauty is the landscape he moves within. She has broken from the mould he had shaped for her, and sits now in the shade of his spent love, cool, prepared, perfectly posed. *For all that you are there, yet I am here, and here will I always stay.*

Arriving

The arriving is finally night. There is no doubt that the day has gone and that this is the time for sleep. But this is when the train has found its stopping point. There is suddenly a speeding up to gather together the strewn pieces of the journey – the washbags, water bottles, scarves, sleeping clothes crumpled on the mattress – and the squeal of the train and jolt of its stopping. The door cranks open and there are gridded steps opening out and ending in space, and a great empty falling between them and the platform. And beyond that, in the dark in a circle around the open door, there are shapes of people waiting, silently waiting, their coats and hats marked in the train lights as the start of autumn. As they come forward their faces become distinctive in the light; from flat to round, from dark to colour, from a shape without eyes to the windows that let us in.

The immigration hall

So in the flow of all of us coming from several directions and pouring into one wide over-full chaotic place and shouted at by women with tucked in uniforms and hard eyes, I am syphoned off to another area, just by accident, the divide random amongst us all, and we all faceless, hardened by confusion, and all of us displaced, those who are not at home. So we are in some other sideways area of the great low humming room, so many of us we are noses in the necks of our neighbours, pushing like one animal towards the exits and we notice that each one person is stopped at an exit desk and I count the minutes they are there –two, three, four– their papers opened cover to cover, held up to the light, scanned, translated, re-read with the slowness and moving eyes and finger of the illiterate, then a paper pushed towards the waiting humbled, held up at the counter as if caught by a highwayman, taking the paper in a Cyrillic not understood, pushed a chewed pen to sign a line not explained. I watch the many heads ahead of me and count it will be 4 minutes x at least 30 people so that's 120 minutes, that's two hours to wait at least, and that's if not more of them push in front me and succeed just with the force of their weight, our breathing raising the heat to a pressure in the head, and nowhere to move back, forward, or sideways without the solid sweat of another body. In front of me a woman crumbles and the crowd is forced to push back to make way for her sudden sitting on the cold floor. Then the crowd as human divides between those angry at the closing of space, those indifferent and just jostling for room to breathe, and those who suddenly care and push towards her to cradle her head and lay their arm under her shoulders to heave her up and those laying what rag they can find to wipe the sweat from her head. And those that leap forward make a bond of solidarity as the kind ones, and stand as a new barricade against pushing. The others become aware kindness might have been useful for them but already it is too late, already the crowd has divided into these three and we have chosen which animal we are to be in this unmaking of us all.

Amber

By the time the Baltic Queen arrived in Newcastle, Motek was sick of England. It was too far away, and in between it and the place he knew was a black stewing broth that never stood still. When Minka told him they had arrived at the wrong bit of England for the white cliffs, his disgust with England became irredeemable.

The first time he stepped on English soil, it rocked like the boat, and he had the sense that the island floated about like a lily pad on which he had only a wobbly foothold. It took three days for the island to stop rocking, and then it stuck solid and immoveable as a lump of ancient granite. But now Motek was sucked into a universe with tall men who mouthed words at him and a sky as tight and grey as a clam, and he fell asleep in a big car that smelt of diesel. and seats that squeaked and scratched.

When Minka shook him awake they had arrived at their new home. At first, Motek thought the whole house was his home, but when they went through the door into an empty hall, and climbed the stairs, and opened another door, he realised that home didn't begin until here. Inside it was like a coffin, lined with a kind of padded wallpaper, just the shape for a human being with no worldly possessions but a soul. The boxes they had carried with them on the ship were bigger than the three rooms they now called home. If Motek joined together all the boxes and climbed inside, he could make a bigger home than the one they now had.

He stood on the landing and watched the boxes being carried up the stairs, one, and another, and another. A lady in a coat with a fox collar appeared from the street, pulling a little boy by the hand. From the boy's coatsleeves dangled knitted gloves on tapes. They began to mount the stairs, squeezing alongside the men as they struggled with the boxes. They climbed the stairs slowly, the little boy puffing and complaining, and the mother with her head averted, so she did not need to look at the boxes, or Sol who was organising them, shouting from the doorway.

Now Minka opened up the boxes, one by one, starting with the highest and working down. Motek sat in the middle of the floor and watched as home was rebuilt around him, strangely telescoped and jumbled. The Hungarian pottery appeared first, decorated with tiny delicate roses; huge winter coats that stood up alone like Russian bears, a rosewood writing desk that unfolded with honey-coloured inlays, two matching chairs with heavy walnut backs and seats with large cabbage-like flowers that someone had picked out painstakingly in green wools. The room began to fill with the musty smell he knew, the same touch of perfume from the rosewood desk where inks had been spilt, the same memory of herring and coconut biscuits in the tea plates. It was oddly reassuring, and Minka and he knew this, that the angle of the photos on the cabinet mattered, the plates needed to be stacked in the same ways as home, with the saucers in their own little pile, and the soup plates stacked on the tea plates. .

It was in that first evening, when the world still rolled like the sea, that Motek and Minka worked their way to the box at the base of the pyramid marked TRADE. They prowled around it, at the nails banged flat against the wood and the steel straps clamping it shut. Because they remembered the last swan on the sands from which all riches were dredged, because they wanted it nearer, in this very room, this was the box of boxes.

Minka was strong as any man, and the nails in the wrench creaked like mice as she bent them back, and they strained together against the threads until a crack of light spread around the lip of the box, and they could prise it open and stare, gaping into the opened place. Inside was a cave of luminous amber, a huge creation workshop of shapes and colours lifted from the electric beaches, polished so their dull coats had fallen away to reveal their inner wildlife trapped in liquid dances, arabesque flies and minute mite constellations, a breathless undersea museum, his Baltic, his captured globs of sun.

Motek kneeled beside the box. Here was his planet, the sealed golden heart of the Elderkind dynasty.

We arrived - England

How did my brother get a visa? He was tall
and ginger, they said he would be
a good Norwegian, so the false-paper-maker
made him a Norwegian passport, got him a
new name, he left the country
as a Norwegian egg-exporter, tried not to speak
in Polish, Yiddish or any language.

Could we work? The visas to England gave us
six months, forbade us gainful employment.
The inspectors came to the factory, saw
him covered in oil, said they would send him away
if they caught him again working. Did they catch him?
Yes. Did they send him away? Yes, they sent him
to Manchester. What next?

Starting out in Manchester
he cut leather jackets
but for every two the other workers made
he made five so they didn't like it,
ganged up and stole his tools.

So what next? He took live chickens
in paper bags to the kosher butcher. One day
in the bus the chicken flew out the bag,
flapped all round the bus. So what next?

He learnt to ride a bicycle, picked it up,
fell off, picked it up, fell off, learnt to ride,
took the chickens in the basket to the kosher butcher.

So what next? Machines arrived for paper-making
from Poland and they began to make paper: but who
needs paper in the war? Blackout! We need blackout!
So they blacked the paper,
made enough in a week to feed the whole family
                                    for six months.

No time for play, we worked seven days a week,
Saturdays their working day, Sunday ours,
I studied every day, seven days a week,
learnt English from nothing in six months.
No time for friends, what was I to do with friends?

And no-one says, and no-one asks,
and were you happy?
Yes, *he would have said.*
Yes, I survived.

We arrived - Japan

Julek in Japan

On February 13th 1941 we sailed overnight to Japan. The boat before us had sailed to Tsuruga, the port in Japan, and been refused entry. It turned around and came back to Vladivostok. Our boat, thank God, sailed without trouble and arrived in the morning in Tsuruga. From there we were taken by train to Kobe. When we arrived there were lots of people on the platform waiting for us – many people I knew from the refugee club in Vilnius, like Ludwik.

Four Russian Jewish families from Harbin had organised the whole community of refugees in Kobe. They had found houses for us, organised food, gave us money, even baked bread for us. They managed two thousand people who came through from Russia to Japan, booking houses all around the city. The chief of the families was a completely bald man.

Ludwik had been quite right about the stamps. We were able to sell our stamps for a good price in Osaka, to local philatelists. Osaka was very busy, with ships constantly sailing in and out of the harbour. We didn't meet Japanese people, except at the public baths. They would separate the women's section from the men's with a piece of string. We couldn't work while we were in Japan and didn't really have our own places to cook. I gave English lessons, but I only knew just a few more words English than my students. The class was quite successful. First of all I had twenty in my class, but they dropped quite soon to five.

Letters were still arriving for me from home. Celina wrote many letters, imagining I was having a glamorous and exciting life in Japan. She and my parents had moved to a small hut outside Krakow, in a place called Bochnia. She told me nothing about what was happening and the news in Japan was not clear either

Ludwik in Japan

I felt a bit lost in Japan and didn't know quite how to behave. I was selling stamps. I travelled to Yokohama, Kyoto and Osaka to philatelist shops. I used the language of hands as we had no shared language, just 'thank you' and 'good bye.' I was never invited into a Japanese home, but I went into many homes of the Harbin Jews. We didn't celebrate any of the festivals; it was a very secular life. I didn't really like the Japanese food, rice or raw fish; so we walked a lot, sat in coffee shops making one coffee last all day, played cards with other displaced people. 90% of the refugees were men. The women had stayed at home with their children. We had very little news about what happened to our families in Europe. I sent home parcels of tea, coffee and food regularly. I knew the parcels arrived as we always received confirmation; but they told us nothing about what was happening. We received letters too. My parents went to Bochnia to visit Julek's parents. They wrote and told me how they had made friends because of Julek and I.

From the divided city

The new child came as a pale survivor
from a split city, and because I saw
the wall in him, how it peeled
and quartered the heart

I became his words: *hello - goodbye*
        playtime   dinner time
        time for home

as he felt for them
in the limbo land
amongst the fixity of desks
the day's white noise
        I am Turkey
        I am Turkish

holding memories hotly in his fist
like a shell, its memory of sea
and I, the other side,
waving, asking him to leap.

One half

Turgay learnt about England from his mother's new friend, Tom. When they went to his first football match, his first seaside running alongside, his first sight of a cricket match on a village green with everything bright from the sun – somehow those days with this new 'friend' who 'liked his mother' made him able to pretend this was home. That's why he would run out the door without a thought for his mother, without looking back, shedding all the ways she fussed over him, the way she knew lapses and messes in detail, fretted too much over his successes and failures.

Today they were going fishing for the first time, by the bridge where the Sunday fishermen lined up with their woolly hats, thermos flasks and bags full of lines, hooks, feathers and flies. Turgay and Tom sat for a while on the low wall of the bridge watching them, and the sluggishly flowing river below. He swung his legs, this strange English man next to him, not asking questions – side by side, letting each other think to themselves whatever they needed to.

He kicked his legs, heard the chatter of the fishermen drifting up, and in the hum of the day felt his shoe loosen, kicked again for fun, felt it dislodge and felt the freedom of kicking, the anger of it. For a moment he didn't care about consequences, though the shoe was making its way down his foot, was now suspended on his toes, and then even that weight was too much and it fell off in slow motion, revealing a shamefully stripy sock known only to himself and his mother. With fascination he followed its motion off the bridge as it spiralled toes first down to the river, and then plop into the brine.

"Oh you've done it now," Tom said.

"Don't worry mate, we'll grab it", shouted the fisherman from the bank.

But the shoe had picked up the fast stream, falling over the rocks and bumped itself downstream. They threw out their lines but it pulled away from them faster than their line could reach. Tom ran down to the riverbank and chased the shoe along the bank, as it twisted and turned over the rocks and into the stream. He was calculating, "Is the river deep? Should I jump in? Is it worth the risk for a shoe? It is only a shoe after all."

As the tide picked it up and flung it over the other side of the fall, he gave up, looked up at Turgay anxiously watching from the bridge, and shrugged. "Sorry, lad, it's gone," his look said.

For Turgay a great emptiness washed over him. It was impossible then to understand it; it was not that his mother would be angry, though indeed she would be. It was rather an indication of things that could not be cured, things that could never be mended. It seemed that he remembered something, another half that he could not reach. In this reaching out for memory, the air around his stripy sock was strangely cool and naked and exposed, strangely mismatching the other foot. It was a lost shoe, just a lost shoe, Tom was saying. *But no,* his heart cried out, *I have lost something much more and I can't remember what it is.*

People who arrive

Information courtesy of the Susser Archive
https://www.jewishgen.org/jc.uk/susser/thesis/thesischa
ptertwopartone.htm

Isaac Polack of Penryn

Isaac Polack of Penryn in Cornwall most respectfully acquaints those Mercantile Gentlemen who have connections in foreign countries, such as France, Germany and Holland, that he writes and translates into English (and vice versa) letters, invoices, bills of trading and other incidental circumstances of commercial intercourse, stiled in either the French, High German or low Dutch languages, with the utmost propriety and expedition.

Elias: Jeweller from Portugal, arrived Port Isaac 1762

Most well instructed and very free in speech on political subjects. His dress was most continental, so you might say, in Louis XIV fashion, waistcoat the same, breeches with buckles fastening at the knee, long wool stockings with shoes and heavy large white metal buckles. His hair, with a long quantity behind the neck, laid with a large black ribbon in a knot and white necktie, very ample, folding around the throat and half covering up the chin.

Abraham Jonas, watchmaker from Portugal, arrived St. Ives 1769

Foreign looking gentleman with black eyes and hair and complexion between dark and fair. Well, you could say his features are very strong, serious you would say but a pleasant expression when amused. He is often amused.

Shemoel Hirsch, tailor from Germany, arrived Plymouth 1781

I arrived like this, with a pair of German boots to the knees and a tassel to each of the tops, a pair of small clothes, black silk waistcoat, lead nankeen longcoat down to my heels, any laps or opening behind and a hat a small crown and wide brim.

E. A. Ezekiel spectacle merchant from France, arrived Land's End 1796

I sell spectacles mounted in silver, tortoiseshell and steel reading glasses, Claude Lorraines, opera glasses, acromatic telescopes, magic lanterns, microscopes, wheel and pediment barometers, and thermometers for the hot-house or brewery.

Rhubarb seller from Turkey

When I go across the country of England I never stay long any one place because I do business there. I lodged once in Taunton at a House where a woman kept a lodging house and buy spices of me.

Another people: A small play

In 1715, the tin mine owner Sir Francis Bassett of Tehidy needed expert engineers to improve the smelthouse between Hayle and Penzance.

THE CAST

Brown, the foreman of the smelthouse

Bassett: the tin mine owner

Becher: the German engineer

3 further German engineers

EPISODE 1:

Brown: Sir, I've heard tell from what I've heard, of a fine man for the smelting and underground work, a Mr. Becher as they call him in his country sir. I have heard him and his men what is with him to be prime performers of the smelting and underground work. This is what I have heard tell, sir.

Bassett: Which is his country, Brown?

Brown: Prussia I believe sir, where they speak the Germany language.

Bassett: Search him out and with all inducements. Invite him here. He will have the best wages and conditions if he can bring his skills to serve us.

EPISODE 2:

Brown: Indeed sir, may I present you Herr Becher as they call him in Germany where he comes from.

Bassett: Herr Becher is not alone. His fellows also have names.

Engineer 1:   Ezekiel Hermann

Engineer 2:   Solomon Bermatt

Engineer 3:   Benjamin Saloman

Bassett: Mm, a singular set of names. Welcome, we are pleased to have you. How do you find Cornwall?

Becher: I find it very well with the help of the map and the horse who knows the place very well too.

Bassett: I mean, do you like it? Are you content with what you find? Have you seen our towns of Penzance and Hayle, and our fine sea coast?

Becher: I find all of this to be most beautiful. The people are most pale.

Bassett: Pale?

Brown: I think it is a compliment sir. I think he means polite.

Bassett: What do your men say?

Engineers: Sicher, ist wunderbar.

Schon Landschaft, ja.

Bassett: Tell them we have heard from very far of the expertise of you and your men, and we are most proud to have you here in Cornwall. Our language is strange to you?

Becher: I think OUR language is strange to YOU?

Bassett: Yes, quite true, quite true.

(Aside) I never thought of that.

Brown: Before you begin, sirs, to do what you must do, I must explain to you the things you must do, according to our terms and conditions.

Becher: We are pleasing to do these things.

Engineers: Yes, most pleasing.

Brown: First to report to work each day at 6.0 am and to work throughout the day until the day is finished at 6.0 pm or when it is dark, whichever is the later, which it is later in the summer months.

Becher and the engineers: Ja, ja, sehr gut, sicher.

Brown: Second, to return all tools, torches, knives and other such to the toolhouse at the end of each day and none to be removed inadvertently or by accident to your home where you might be living, or left in the mines.

Becher et al: Ja, ja. Was sagt er? Spater sagen wieder.

Brown: Third, to report to work each day excepting the Sabbath day which is a day of rest.

Becher et al: Alles gut, verstanden.

Brown: So you report Monday to Saturday, each of the days therewith, in the terms and conditions what we have laid out, as many hours of the daylight as we need for the work.

Becher et al: (in some consternation) Was sagt er? Samstag? Hat er Samstag gesagt?

Becher: We say we do not report to work on Saturday. We are sorry but we cannot do this.

Brown: Excuse me, sir, these terms and conditions what are here laid out are not for you inadvertently or otherwise to change.

Becher: Our day for resting is

Engineers: Samstag

Becher: Saturday. But on Sunday it is good we work.

Brown: No Sunday it is not good you work. It is good that you work on Saturday.

Becher: Nein, entschuldigung, this is your Sabbath but ist unfortunately to say not ours. Und we will not work on this day which is our Sabbath.

EPISODE 3

Brown: Sir, these people are most inconvenient sir, in fact, not to put too fine a point on it, they are a trouble sir.

Bassett: They have hardly arrived, Brown. You have hardly spoken to them more than a few words and they to you a few words you cannot understand. So how can they be so quickly a trouble?

Brown: In German, sir, Saturday is Sunday, so to speak; and Sunday is Saturday. And I can't be having that.

Bassett: In German you say this is so?

Brown: Indeed it seems to me sir. I never been having before in English such a strange and untoward problem. They will not work on the Saturday, being the day they do not work. But they say that to work on Sunday is good, which it is not.

Bassett: I wonder Brown, does the tin know which day it is, Saturday or Sunday?

Brown: This is, for you if I may say so sir, a most unlikely question, because of course sir, the tin thinks nothing at all.

Bassett: So if the tin was struck on Sunday, it would be just the same as if it was struck on Saturday?

Brown: For the tin it would sir.

Bassett: And for whom, then, would it not be the same?

Brown: Well as I said, sir, it would be most untoward.

Bassett: For you, Brown, it would be most untoward. For the tin, and for the mines, and for the people who purchase the tin, there will be no sign of its iniquity, not a single marking. Instead there will be engineers who are content to work in the Bassett tin mines and will do so with great success and for many years. So what do you think is the solution to your trouble, Brown?

EPISODE 4

6 months later. New furnaces have been built, the smelthouse expanded, and the rest day changed from Sunday to Saturday.

Bassett: Brown, had you noticed the habits these engineers have at the dinner table?

Brown: They eat most polite sir, not dripping their food hardly at all, and then neat onto their aprons.

Bassett: Brown, why is it you have not already made it your business to know these people?

Brown: They are very close, they seem quite close in together.

Bassett: If you do not speak to them, how do you know?

Brown: I do speak to them sir, but not on private matters. At work I speak to no-one about private matters. At work, I speak about work, sir.

Bassett: You are dutiful to a fault, Brown. Now, had you not noticed at the dinner table how the men spurn to eat the meat of the pig. Time after time, they smile at us and say ja but leave the meat standing in gravy on the plate.

Brown: I did not think it my business to look on their plate, sir.

Bassett: And yet, when I offer them herrings and mackerel, they eat like it is their last day on earth?

Brown: So do we all I think sir. Yourself, of course, excepting; most polite.

Bassett: And what do you think all this is on account of? The Saturday Sabbath, the spurning of the pork, the eating of mackerel, the lighting of candles on Friday night?

Brown: What is it on account of? I've never been seeing anyone here what had less than two plates of pork at table, sir, where possible. Maybe they have weak digestion, sir, from Germany.

Bassett: I think not, Brown. I think we have another thing here altogether. I think it is their religion.

Brown: A most strange religion, I'll say, to do with dinner plates.

Bassett: Indeed the dinner table is a place where we are who we are. They are Jews, Brown. And you will find out more, and speak it back to me. Find out where they pray, and how they pass their Sabbath. I wish them to know I am a friend and I understand their traditions belong to those of the Children of Israel and the people for whom our own holy Son was one.

Francis Bassett's family papers show that he had a small synagogue built for the tinminers' community somewhere between Camborne and Hayle. The symbol of the Pascal lamb, centre of the table during the Jewish Passover service, became the trademark for the smelthouse. The symbol of the lamb was smelted onto every block of tin. A hostelry built for the workers was called The Lamb and Flag and the inn, which still bears that name, uses the smelthouse symbol as its sign.

All our voices

The children

Papa my hair has grown long
and my shoes have opened at the toe
my case with the steel corners, its handle
has broken.
A tooth came out, Papa.
My hair has grown long and I have no combs.

The father

I am wondering
what would be left of me if were stripped
of what it is Russian in me.
First the language, rusty and neglected;
the birch forests, ice lakes, the cakes of
bird's milk.
Were I to lose it, the language,
the landscape, I would be bereft.

The bureaucrat

The immigrants are quiet, inoffensive and industrious, making
the most of what they earn and generally abstemious as
regards intoxicating liquors it being seldom they are seen the
worse for drink in the streets.

The arrivees

I can make hats
felt hats
measuring caps, pasting tickets, stretching furs, nailing furs,
making fur trims, pasting buckram, hanging pieces, drying
pieces,
pressing pieces, moulding pieces, turning on gas jets.
heating the press, trimming the edges, sewing the edges
by hand.

*Jewelers, ladies' tailors, mineral water makers, pipe makers, pouch
makers, pressers, potters, printers, rabbis, rope-makers, saddlers, seamen,
ritual slaughterers, soap-boilers, scribes, stick makers, surgeons, tallow
chandlers, tanners, teachers*

We made cigarettes –
you paid by the weight, hand-made cigarettes -
the papers were stuck around them,
they had a long stick and thing called 468.
You pushed the tobacco up through the stick,
It used to be all flat, more flat than round.
They used these scissors with curved ends.
You could print your name on the papers –
        If you were rich enough you could!

*tinkers, tobacco cutters, traders, turners, umbrella makers, upholsterers,
varnishers, watchmakers, clockmakers, waterproofers, weavers,
woodcutters*

I will make for thee
rendered goose with chrain
cucumber in sour cream
schmaltz herring filleted, skinned and soaked
with a squeeze of lemon
petchach and Russian pies
leber mit tzibbeles liver with large onions
cholent pearl barley and haricot beans
potato kugel with chicken fat and one mild grated onion
lokshen kugel with savoury noodles
tzimmes with carrots
tzimmes with pumpkin
white cabbage sauerkraut
red cabbage sweet kraut with apple
kreplach stuffed with cheese
kishke flour and onion sausage for cholent.

Sadie daughter of Ezekiel from Kovno has been a scholar in this school since 1909. Her record for conduct, work, regularity and punctuality is an excellent one. As one of the senior scholars, she has proved herself most loyal and helpful. Her books have always been kept neatly and well. Her needlework is excellent.

Après le deluge – Paris 1949

The chic old lady with chiseled features, neat tweed coat and stick walks each day up the Rue Clair and down. Here is her sea, her shoal of weathered stones, the daily stalls of fish, cheese, fruit, flowers, meats and meringues. She buys two bunches of fat asparagus stalks, stops to shake hands with a man in a black coat, a white hat and white scarf in dapper ensemble. He greets her formally, with respect, she likewise calling him *monsieur*, her banker who knows what there is to hide and to remember, and the birth of the tweed coat and its insecurities. They walk on in opposite directions, each triggering for the other a train of memory that takes them into awkward cul-de-sacs they prefer to avoid, and she does so by looking over the trays of cooked Asiatic dishes, but with no intention to eat, so when the solicitous vendeur says, "Madam?" she returns a watery, distant smile for the sake of politeness and moves on, for this is her engager sans engager, where she is known and not known. Those she had loved most chose to leave, or death removed them too soon or too fast, without proper farewells.

She leaves white lilies in the hook on the wall every year to fill the space, but it does not, and sometimes she feels the bullet holes with her fingers wondering how small they have become, how hard they are now to see after all these years since the time when the breaks in the wall seemed like the gates of Hell yawning to pull her in. The man in the white hat and scarf walks on, stops at the newsstand in front of the headlines of the Parisien that reads:

Etes-vous superstitieux? Vendredi le 13

Non he thinks, digging his hands into his silk-lined pockets. *Thankfully, not at all – pas du tout.*

But he hurries on, without stopping to buy a newspaper as he usually did.

Peace Oak

Planted for his son, lost in WWI 1919

The tree has spread strong arms since its sapling start
when you dug the tines into the earth,
feeling it kinder by far than that other earth.

Did you feel anger at its indifference
as you opened the earth, its mechanism
of worms, the tunnels and paths of its inner life,

or did the earth even then let you in
to its chance of peace, receiving the roots
as you laid them gently into ground,

that mound of earth a place of renewal,
an echo of that other place that ended all.
The century has given

what it took away: the acorn
planting its roots deeply, lifting its arms widely
growing like hope towards the sun.

Border Control - Israel/Jordan border 2007

The falls were just the other side of the line, so near they were overlooked. Those who passed the falls were either in a hurry to leave, or in a hurry to arrive; or otherwise, were posted there to police both directions. The water rushed onto a deep shelf, wide enough for swimming, wide enough to feel safe, where the moving veil of water became still for a while before gravity pulled it onward over the stones.

Agnes was swimming in the warm pool, and its water moved in circles around her wherever she stood, holding, lifting, making her weightless. There was a young man there too, jumping in and out of the rush of the waterfall, screaming with the shock and the cold rush and crash of it, in and out, holding his head under the gush. He did not take any notice of her, sharing this neglected shelf of water, and she was glad to be invisible, slightly shocked by the water. This had become her home, this side of the border. Men like this had always divided her from those she loved. They probably hardly knew why, and when they did, it was under orders. She had forgiven them. He could have been her son, had he lived. He was chestnut brown, his arms those that had carried and weighed and struggled. She noticed his leaping games with danger, in contrast to her safe paddling in the warm inner circle. His shrieks of delight bounced across the water like a pebble.

A forked twig was carried into her path and then pulled into the magnetism of the flow: she watched it ride on the spray, catch on a rock, come unloose again, snap into halves as it trailed helplessly the water's forward crash. As if in strange sympathy with the stick she moved to the edge of the circle of water that held her safely, and further towards it, and broke its outer edge. The effect was instant, and unforgiving. The magnetic pull picked her up, steered her into its force, and she was part of its shocking, inescapable crash over the ledge. As animals might do, she seemed to float above herself, her limbs turning to a soft vessel of herself, so she was not inside her own bones as they banged over the rocks and on in the violent shove of water.

The next thing she knew was a bruising hold under her shoulders, clamped to a body that had no denial, that steered her to the shore. She was a creature being rescued by another; they were pared back to their essential of being alive, both of them. The earth came up again and held her body, laid her out. She entered her broken and bruised bones reluctantly, found the moaning she heard came from her own lips, and the drumming sensation was her own arm trembling almost rhythmically against the ground.

Beside her the young man was sitting on his haunches, looking at her through the long tunnel of their separate senses. He wiped his hand across his brow. His eyes were matt with a profound tiredness. He was 23, had fought in wars, and never knew for which side he fought. He was tired of what he had seen. These were his days of respite. Here he longed not to care, not to rescue, not to die, not to cause to die. He wanted to shout with joy under the freedom of the cascade.

"I am sorry," she said, quietly.

Because they did not even share a language, he did not know how to say it. All these years, they had been trying to teach him to believe in causes. He did not believe a word of it. He couldn't see, hear, smell or touch causes. Not like the water as it crashed on him and cleaned him inside and out. And now, now there were no causes. "No, **I** am sorry", he said.

Going away

"Don't say a word," she said, as he struggled to speak, so much of him now attending to the act of breathing. She put a finger over his lips: "just quiet now, just quiet." It calmed him, gave him permission to give the heft of his head back to the pillow. The son Harry, now grown and tall, watched this final journey and struggled to see the father without his demons, as he should have been, as he had been born. He would say *it wasn't me, I never fitted in, I tried but I carried what I left behind, what could I do? What else to do with time but drink it?* The family had scattered like a diaspora to escape this devil's pact – he, loss of hope, the bottle; and though there was nothing good about that, yet it was the best they could do to survive.

Something about the mother's forgiveness made him the child again, that day he had not understood, when he was hardly three years old. He was in his high chair, reaching for that golden spill that was egg yolk. Somehow, he knew something was wrong, the egg cup smashed into pieces against the wall, mother picking up the pieces, her hands shaking, turning over each broken shard. It seemed to be part of something loud and crashing and uncomfortable that came to their house. Both father and mother seemed to be afraid of it. It was a thing that made them mad, made them shout and break plates. Sometimes he thought it was an invisible monster. It hid during the day, while he played in his sandpit and mother measured ladies for new skirts. Sometimes he hid at tea time when father did magic tricks, pulled pennies out of his ear and made marbles disappear. But then, sometimes it sprang out of the walls unexpectedly and then everybody went mad.

That day, the monster had filled every corner of the house and made all of them scream. Though he couldn't see it, he knew it was there, strangling them all.

"We must go, baby," mother had said. "We must go."

She let him throw toys into the open bag, a handful of dinosaurs, a sheep with half a bitten ear. "Not the train," she said, "it's too big". In the bag were also T-shirts, shorts, socks and all other manner of useless items that would easily have left room for his train, and tank engine too. But something held in, urgent, in her voice made him feel there was no point arguing, and no time to cry. She pulled the front door closed behind her, suitcase on wheels in one hand, he in the other wearing his Tigger rucksack, wearing his coat with the furry hood and itchy collar.

First they stayed with Aunty Andrea, but Aunty said terrible things about father. Mother screamed what a good heart he had, how hard he tried, how much he loved us, "how good he is with Harry," then ran up to her room and locked the door. And then Harry would hear her sobbing, just as she had done when the monster came to their house. So that wasn't good. Then they stayed in a kind of home where mother said they would find "peaceandquiet." But in this "peaceandquiet" place were three other mothers each with babies who screamed and spat out their food and threw their toys on the floor, so that wasn't good either. Then they went to a guesthouse where Harry was ordered out of the sitting room because it was 'private' and then he was ordered to stop playing on the stairs because they were 'public' and the guests were tripping over him.

And then one day, mother scooped him up in her arms and said, "Would you like to see daddy again?"

They caught the bus home. Tigger had lost an ear, mum's suitcase had lost a wheel and dragged along the street like a reluctant poodle. Though their walk down the street was more bedraggled than the walk up the street one month earlier, there was a kind of comfort in it.

When they opened the door, he was there, dad, sitting on the sofa half asleep, football playing in a muffled way on the TV. He had tried, you could see that. There was a torn-open packet of digestive biscuits next to him on the sofa, the ash tray was full of cigarette butts. But they were not bottles. It was an act of love that they were not bottles, a way of bringing us home. He started up as they came in, his face moving through a kaleidoscope, starting with a sunburst of joy Harry would never forget; moving rapidly on to surprise, relief, guilt, pride in his dry month, then anger and, liking that place, finished there. He opened his mouth to speak.

"Don't say a word," his mother said, "Just quiet now, just quiet."

It is those words they wept for now, his life, her forgiveness, and how hard they all tried.

Musical chairs

Reza had been just fine at school until Maisie's birthday party. He had chosen the present for Maisie from the toyshop, a set of balloons which blew up into different animal shapes. The shopkeeper had shown him how it started, as a sticky limp blob and then wheezed and puffed itself into a huge stretched dinosaur with squeaky skin and a big plastic smile. So Saria couldn't understand why Reza was so downcast when she picked him up at 5.0 with the other parents after the party. Was it the other children? Had they been unkind to him and pushed him out of their games? Had Maisie laughed at him or her mother or father told him off for making too much noise? Had he broken something and was afraid to tell anyone? No, it was none of those and Saria was puzzled. When she met Maisie's mother at the school-gates on Monday she gently sounded her out.

"Oh, thank you so much Mrs. Parkes for the party. Reza did have a nice time. Did he join in OK and behave himself?"

"Oh yes, he's a lovely boy and seems to get on so well with the other children. They all seem to love him!" Mrs. Parkes said. So that wasn't it.

Reza seemed to forget about it for the next few weeks, going to school happily, even letting go of her hand before they reached the school gates and running towards them himself. She saw Maisie hugging him, and the teacher kindly ruffling his hair with her hand, saw the way he proudly brought his paintings home with him at the end of the day, and his writing book with stories about dogs and fire engines and policemen, all copiously illustrated with pencil drawings.

He was happy, in fact, until the next birthday party, which was Hugo's. Before Hugo's party, Saria could see he was getting agitated and panicky.

"Maybe I shouldn't go," he said.

"Why darling, don't you like Hugo?"

"No, I **do**", Reza said adamantly. So that wasn't it.

"Shall we choose Hugo a birthday present?"

That cheered up Reza, and he chose a silver mouth organ which the shopkeeper demonstrated to him in quite a spectacular way, making all the children in the shop gather round and beg their mothers to buy one.

When Saria arrived to pick him up at the end of the day, Reza was sitting on the floor amongst the other children, absorbed in a Punch and Judy show just coming to its denouement at a makeshift theatre built with cardboard boxes and tablecloths. He was shouting at Judy, warning her about the truncheon that had appeared on the end of Punch's arm in the background.

"Look! Over there! Over there!" but Judy pretended not to hear.

Hugo's father crouched behind the boxes with a puppet on each hand, gave Judy the victory, turning on Punch and beating him offstage with her plaster fists to the delight of all the children, including Reza.

So when she and Reza walked home hand in hand, Reza clutching his going-home bag of paper hats, crackers and sweets, she was reassured.

"Did you like it sweetie?"

"Yes, a **lot**!" he said, with a kind of painful passion.

But when she opened the front door into their dark mezzanine, the carpet still marked and smelling with the rice pudding Rufus the cat had trodden round the flat, room by room, the twilight casting the small-windowed hallway into even greyer gloom, Reza burst into tears. As Saria held him close, murmuring, "What is it darling? Did something happen at the party?" it just made his tears more passionate and his heaving chest more agitated, so he was gasping for breath, his face soaking his shirt with tears.

She waited, just holding him, rocking him as she had when he was a baby, stroking his hair gently, gently. Then she heard his words gasping up out of the storm.

"They all have big houses, Maisie and Hugo," he was saying. "When I have my party there isn't a big r—r—r—room."

She rocked him, just let him talk, say whatever he liked.

"They all have parties in big rooms but when it's my party we won't have a big room," he sobbed. "If I want Maisie and Hugo and Henry and Tara to come, we won't have a big room!"

This list of names seemed to bring up an even deeper agony of loss, and he sobbed again in little short gasps for breath. She knew there was something more to come, waited for it.

"Their daddies do Punch and Judy shows and magic tricks," he sobbed.

Saria rocked him and they both knew everything had been said and there was something like a black sink about the absences he had opened up. They were just there and truths, like Hugo's funny clever dad with wonderful glove puppets was a truth; or like Maisie's big house with a sitting room, French windows and a rose garden was a truth. Their little mezzanine with bunk-beds and no catflap or dad, that was a truth too. They did not need to say so, because they understood each other so well.

"You know what, sweetie," Saria said, "we can have your party in the pizza parlour. What about that?"

"But there will be all the other people having pizza!" he sobbed. But he was thinking about it, she could tell. It was opening up a little glimmer in all the hopeless dark clouds crashing around his broken heart.

"We can hire it just for us. Did you know we could do that?! It will be just Reza's party for the day, Reza's pizza parlour."

"Will it?" Reza asked, in spite of himself, stopping in the downward rush of his tears.

"Yes, of course! We can do that! We can hire it for the very day of your birthday, and everyone can have as much pizza as they like. And we can ask Hugo's dad to do the Punch and Judy show for us. Now how good is that!"

Reza began to rub his eyes dry with the coiled soft side of his fists.

"Can we?" he asked. "Can we ask for another puppet show, not Punch and Judy? Can we have Tarzan?"

On the day of the party, Reza spun between wild excitement, jumping on Rufus the cat to make his tail curl, spinning round and round the flat singing happy birthday to himself; and anxiety that his friends would come to his home instead of the pizza parlour by mistake, that the pizza parlour would be full of other people talking and laughing and drinking coca cola and there would be no room for him and his friends, or that Hugo's father would do Punch and Judy again by mistake when they all knew the story already.

But Mr. Kovacs had been happy to prepare a new cast of puppets and a new transportable cardboard theatre, and had insisted on helping Saria with party games too. When the pizza parlour opened its doors to Saria, Reza, Mr. and Mrs. Kovacs and Hugo, it was thrilling that the whole big, enticing crusty-pizza smell was his. He and Hugo ran screeching round the room until the pizza chef came out of the kitchen and scolded them. All his class arrived –Maisie, Razmi, Henry brought his little sister Katy– but the more arrived, the quieter Reza became. Saria noticed him move from the centre of the room where he had been running with Hugo, into the corner as the children arrived with their brightly-wrapped presents in their hands, their crisp shirts and new dresses with matching shoes. It's fine, Saria thought. It's where he wants to be. It will all sort itself out. I was like that at his age.

The party games were a triumph. They began by passing the balloon round a circle with their noses, making squeaks and pops, some deliberate so they could all scream with laughter as the balloons zizzed in loud farting noises. Then they had a wheelbarrow race in pairs, one walking along the floor with their hands while the other held their legs from behind. Everyone was having a grand time, even Reza whose birthday it was, occasionally forgot himself and threw himself wholeheartedly and uproariously into the games.

The last one Saria had planned was Musical Chairs. The chairs were all pulled into the circle and Saria was going to manage the music, turning it on and off at strategic moments while Mr. Kovacs was going to pull out a chair each time the music started until there was only one chair and one child left. There was lots of chatter and laughter, jiving to the music, clutching too slowly at chairs with shouts of "Cheat! Cheat!", shoving each other out of the way with sharp elbows and strong knees. Mr. Kovacs refereed these sometimes violent exchanges as the circle narrowed and the disgruntled outcasts amused themselves, either by shouting at those still remaining or throwing themselves at the pizza. So it was only gradually in this melee that Saria realised what was happening to Reza. As the music stopped each time he was flitting, nimble as a gadfly into the nearest chair, undercutting his neighbours so seamlessly they conceded and each time he would look at them and shrug as if to say, "I couldn't help it."

Now the bystanders were growing to be most of the party, as the competition became hotter and closer, and they began taking up the chant, "Re-za! Re-za!" Though he pretended this was of no consequence, Reza was flushed pink and his eyes were sparkling. Now he began his little short gasps as he realised it was just him and Maisie with her swinging plaits and black squeaky shoes. Now it was just one chair left in the middle and Saria, not wanting to look as she hit the start/stop button. She turned her back, to be fair to both Reza and Maisie, and let the music run, to the cheers and shouts from the Reza and Maisie camps. Then she clicked the shutter down, to a roar of laughter and cheers.

Turning round, there she saw him, her boy, his eyes bright with delight, sitting on the central chair, Maisie on his knee where they had thrown themselves in the same split second, the children in a circle around them, clapping and shouting, "Re-za! Re-za!"

"Well, both of them have won, don't you think?" Mr. Kovacs said.

"Re-za! Re-za!" the children shouted,

"Both of us," said Reza, daring to put his arms round Maisie just in case she fell off the chair.

When they got home after the party Saria hugged Reza close.

"You are so brave, Reza," she said.

Reza felt his heart swell with pride. Brave, he thought that was for people who escaped from prison and people who saved other people and suffered for it like daddy.

"You are brave too, mummy," he said.

Friendship

Imre had been sad since the last time he saw his mother, through the train window, standing quite still. He had wondered why it was she had tears running down her cheeks when the journey was to be a short one and the return soon. It had taken a while to understand the truth, and it had arrived slowly, so he could not tell the moment when he realised. But since then all his ways of finding another mother had failed. He was not quite sure why it was that people seemed to melt away from him, just when he was ready to bind them to him forever. Perhaps it was because he wanted to claim them too soon–a few hours or a few days after setting eyes on them: or the reverse, because it took too long–sometimes years, decades to commit, and by the time he did, they had become tired of him and run away.

So it was he lived on his own trying hopelessly to tell his life story to the girl in the supermarket queue in between queuing and checking out, to the postman in between opening the garden gate and dropping the junk mail in his box, to the waitress at the station café in between ordering a coffee and drinking it. Why was it none of them seemed to have time to be interested in his story? Was he doing something wrong? How was it he hadn't learnt the rules for making friends? What was it he had missed out?

So he decided to invite someone new into his life by any means he could, and anyone, anyone at all who would talk to him for more than 5 minutes. The offer online was for a fish tank which would be personally delivered and personally set up in your house by the company at no extra cost. He calculated this would take at least one hour, if he made sure there was furniture that needed clearing and space created in his front room. For start-up customers the local pet shop offered a complementary goldfish and, for a small monthly fee, regular delivery of fish food. The possibility for conversations on a regular basis made the offer irresistible.

On the morning appointed for the arrival of the tank, Imre made a special trip to the supermarket. He bought tea and cream cakes, as well as herbal infusions just in case the delivery man preferred those, and figs and grapes in case he had high cholesterol and was avoiding cream cakes. Imagining what kind of person would ring his doorbell was exciting: whether he would have a great deal of hair or very little, whether he or she would be wearing overalls with the name of the company on them, or just jeans and T-shirt. He liked to think about it, to plan his strategy.

On the appointed day, he waited in the front room with the kettle filled ready to boil and the bags in the teapot. Two minutes before the end of the delivery window the doorbell rang.

"Sorry mate, in a traffic jam," the man said, hardly glancing at him. The boxes came in, the man concentrating totally on his task, not looking to right or left, replying to all Imre's conversation in grunts. Imre began to regret he had made the delivery so complicated there was no time to talk.

"Would you like a cup of tea?" he kept saying, hovering around the doorway as the boxes were unpacked and furniture pulled across the room, and tank assembled on the floor.

"No thanks, mate, need to get this done and on to the next job. Running late now".

Imre watched him, alarmed at the size of the tank assembling in front of his sofa. It seemed to occupy almost the whole extent of the back wall. He watched, helplessly, as the pipes and glass and water filter and pumps all emerged from the packing and began to sculpt themselves into his sitting room.

"Er, do you do this often?" he asked the man, whose head had disappeared behind up a pipe.

Grunt.

Then the fish emerged, in a large plastic bag filled with water, the kind you win at the fair.

"You can tip 'im in," said the hopeless failure of a best friend, "and tip in the food as a starter, 'e'll get used to his new home alright. Keep the light soft, don't dazzle 'im."

"Er, this is the first pet I've ever had," Imre said.

Grunt.

By 12.0 noon the job was done, the front room was transformed into an aquarium with a shiny glass window into an underwater wonderland, and a single golden fish wild with delight sliding from one confection to another. The delivery man refused for the fifth time a cup of tea, asked for Imre's signature on the job record, exchanged invoices and receipts, and before Imre could stop him, was gone.

Imre brought the tea and cream cakes into the room, sat opposite his tank and began to eat them himself, one by one. The golden fish slipped and slithered weightlessly around his new world, travelling through his own planet of baby roots and weeds and rocks, slithering in and out of the branches, diving up to peck at the water surface for imaginary midges. Imre watched fascinated.

"Poor mite, he'll be lonely. I'll need to get him a friend," he said to himself.

Then the fish dived down into the depth of the tank, and swam out to its outer edge, his fins like frills shivering in the water, looking out at the world beyond his window.

They looked at each other, Imre and the fish. And then Imre had a surge of something new he had never felt before.

He wanted the fish to be gloriously alive in his own special way.

He took the remainder of his bun, crumbled it in his hand, and dropped the crumbs onto the surface of the water. Watching the fish follow his hand, draw a golden line up to the surface, and peck at the crumbs with its soft open mouth, made Imre happier than he had been since he was child, and since his mother had laid her hand on his head and said, "I will come to see you and we will buy a brown puppy."

Courtship - Newcastle, 1949

The three young girls were sitting on the wall of Whitley Bay with ice-cream cones, kicking their feet and laughing.

"Did you go out with that foreign boy then, Ena?" Vi asked.

"My what an accent!" said Sheila, "I wonder you understood a word he said!" and they hooted with laughter again.

"I don't know," Ena replied eventually, "I thought he was rather sweet. Though I shan't be seeing him again."

"Why not then, go on, tell us."

"Didn't he kiss well?" said Sheila, taking a big lick from her ice-cream.

"Well he came to the house, all polite, to collect me and ma thought he was quite the gentleman," began Ena.

"Yes, and ----?"

"like proper walking out together, me all dressed up to the nines,"

"What, in the spotty dress, did you?"

"New one with a red belt, my shoes killed me!"

They all knew about shoes that killed them, each of them sitting on the wall.

"Well so far so good by the sounds of it," Sheila said.

"And wasn't there just the longest cinema queue you ever saw!"

"What was it what you saw?"

"Third Man again. Saw it already last week with Alf but pretended I hadn't cos he was trying so hard for a good idea and I didn't want to disappoint him. Anyway, there isn't much else is there round here on a Saturday night."

Vi thought about it, as she bit right down the ice cream cone. "Not if you want to be in the dark!" she shrieked gleefully.

"Go on then Ena, what next? Nothing's gone wrong so far."

"So we waited didn't we in this queue and talked alright, and I liked him I think, his quiet way. Just when we got to the ticket man, up there ---"

"What, he didn't pay?"

"No, it weren't that."

"Go on then,"

"He did pay, but you'll never believe, he had a HANDBAG!"

"What, a handbag?!"

"Yea, he got out this HANDBAG! Honest, it was, I had to look again, then you won't believe it, but he got out a PURSE thing to get out his money."

"A purse?!" Vi echoed, and they creased up, laughing

"Oh my, he had a handbag and a purse!" but this was too funny for words, just too too funny. How could it possibly be, a man with a leather handbag and a purse he took out of it for his money.

"Well I won't be going out with HIM again," said Ena, wiping the last ice-cream crumbs from her lips.

"Well I wouldn't be seen dead with a man with a handbag, that's for sure," Vi said.

"My, what they do in those foreign places!" Sheila said. "You never know, maybe ALL the men have handbags. I bet they do."

Marriage

What a bright girl she had been, with all her future flush and ripe as hope. She loved that flight from the house in the woods, how exactly it felt like moving from the margins to the centre. Where she had grown up it was not-quite: the shops were not quite the places where you could buy the newest styles, and the café not quite the place you would take your boy or he would take you, and the people not quite the ones you would stay for or choose to visit again once you had left home. But here, oh here it was the very thing. There was more to stay for and live for than you could ever discover in one life. You could laugh yourself hoarse, floating from cinema screen to comedy club to champagne bar, and you could burn your weekly pay a hundred times over with the fanciest shoes and best flapper dresses and strings of fake pearls.

And so it was in this heyday that Nadya, whose childhood had been as far from cities as possible, blossomed in the great crest of the city wave, met Fabio also on a great escape, and together they came together in recognition at the Victory dance. They did not know what it was they recognised in one another, or why it mattered so, and made them ache for one another and long to meet again; but it was that both were stretching their hopes into this new land where the shining people lived and it was not quite them, not yet. She, in spite of that, was a gangly, untamed beauty with natural curls that grew pale at the ends as they bleached in the sun, and blue eyes that narrowed with a luminous light even at rest; and he was small and dainty so, as you looked at him, you imagined him in white shoes and a dapper suit and a way of spinning lightly to a tune even when he was still. It was an electricity between them that smouldered wordlessly between first meeting and second, though neither knew why as they seemed to be so physically mismatched and with so little in fact to say to one another and hardly a common language. But it was as if each knew that in another place, in their imagined lives, they were talking about everything under the sun, and laughing one another into hoarseness, and setting all their worlds to rights, trouble by trouble, memory by memory, fear by fear, hope by hope. So the meetings went on, the Mayday dance, and the summer fair, the trip to the circus and the zoo and both of them shivering to the hurt of the elephants and the confinement of gorillas – so they knew they were attuned though it was not said. So when he proposed it was not a surprise, though there had been no talk of love, not yet. It was like a gentle sashaying into the inevitable, it was letting life tumble from stage to stage without resistance – she from Russia who painted ladies' nails, and he a toolmaker exiled forever from Franco's Spain; she on the cusp of city life, he the quiet hopes of the hardworking. They saved up and borrowed and the house that took them to the suburbs was both theirs and the bank's. To share in this way was a revelation and a new kind of hope; their own front door, and porch, and narrow hallway with hooks for coats and a lean-to kitchen with a back door into a grassed courtyard with a washing line and a slatted shed. Though this was not something she ever thought she wanted, now it was here it must of course be her dream. It was what she was meant to dream.

After the wedding, with her still in white lace and satin shoes, he led her over the threshold. She loved him, he was a good man, he had done the good and noble thing as had she, life had only prepared her to be a good woman and now she was grown there was no turning back. The few friends they had, her painted ladies, his neighbours at the factory bench, had witnessed their vows, her lace veil and the white rose petals they dropped along the aisle. So nothing could be amiss, surely.

The day after the wedding was a working day – nothing to be done. His start was early for the factory – 6.0 am when she longed to sleep. Yet she felt to sleep was disloyal, and he was not sure too whether slipping away so early was unloving on their first married day. So both from the first dawn were uneasy, and she was unsure how men liked breakfast. In all her young girl and housemaid years, she hadn't made a man's kind of breakfast. She got up in her dressing gown, yellow still with sleep, her feet on the cold floor making her cough, padding back and forwards in the kitchen.

"Don't to worry," he said, reaching behind her for eggs in the fridge, porridge in the tin. "Nadya, you go sleep and not to worry you."

But she paced back and forwards, watching the competence of his wrist as he broke the egg and spread the yoke in the pan, tossed in the butter and let it sizzle on the flame.

"I can do that," she said, not knowing if indeed she could, and if this early start was something she could bear. Humiliated, she sat by him at the table as he ate his eggs on toast, tinkling fork against plate, and she loved him as dearly as he was new and strange to her. He was so quietly complete, like a creature of another species, and she watched him, wondering where she might fit in that life. He ate silently, as he always had in these early mornings, and quickly, as the minutes were counted in this factory work. Then, finished, the plate now with its layers of grease, he scraped back the chair, pulled his coat off the hall hooks onto his shoulders, leaned forward and kissed her softly, tenderly.

"Goodbye you my wife," he said, "I sorry to go and house new to you and all. But I love you, io ti chiero."

Then he opened the door so the cold early morning blew in its raw darkness and pulled it closed behind him. Now Nadya was frozen to her place. The kitchen had suddenly become shattering in its silence. It refused to move by so much as a twitch. In fact, she realised for the whole day until his return in twelve hours, not a thing would move or make a sound without her making of it. And the only possible makings would be domestic, small ones; the running of a tap, the washing of a dish, the cracking of an egg. In the streets outside were rows and rows of houses just the same as this one, with the same sealing of a life inside its walls and other cycles of small domestic movements silently lived.

"This is marriage," she heard herself say, as if a wise, older self were speaking to this young, bright one that had danced and laughed at the Victory ball. Her heart ached for the sweet man who poached his own eggs, and who was absent, absent, absent. She sat on the kitchen chair and with the despair of the child first left alone in an empty room, remembered what she wanted to say.

"Mama, papa, where are you now? Why am I alone?"

Work

Nadya found a job painting nails for posh weddings. The bride had kindly offered her and Fabio a room in the hotel for the night, she suspected so she could be called on to provide manicures or facials throughout the night for all her friends. She took several hours dressing and making herself up to look as if she was utterly accustomed to such luxury; but in truth neither she nor Fabio had ever even entered the tradesman's entrance of a place like this before, let alone the front entrance. Fabio felt like a burden on this bird of paradise that was his wife. She could look appropriate without saying a word, but he did not have that instant gift, and even worse if he were to speak, his English might remind these terribly well-spoken people of bad sitcoms about Italian waiters. To ensure he always seemed fully occupied, and to drown out the pain of his exclusion, he drank every champagne flute he was offered, he drank to the bride and groom more times than he could count. He found with the wine waiters no words were exchanged, just a look of the eye or a nod and his glass was filled. It was the perfect mime theatre he needed. At midnight, when the party was over, he staggered back to the hotel room, held up by Nadya as the patterned carpet swirled round and round in front of him, and the floor kept lurching upwards as if he was on a very flimsy ferry in a storm. As he fell into the room, the night's consumption pitched itself out of his body with a great bear's groan that burst from the pit of his stomach and emitted itself all over the luxury peacock-feather themed hotel carpet. The last thing he heard before crashing like falling masonry over the bed, was Nadya uttering a cry; and he was dead to the world as she spent the night running in and out of the bathroom with towels and toilet paper, scrubbing the carpet on her hands and knees, her best dress dropped back into the overnight bag like a discarded skin.

"They'll never invite me back now", Nadya grieved.

Fabio just groaned. It entered his heavy head on the pillow. Then he groaned again.

"Where am I?" he said, "where am I?"

Changing names

This name is the one I first heard
as clusters of sounds that meant
me, myself, spoken by those who loved me.

This name was the first I learnt to write,
with lines and circles that made letters
that shafted into my heart, that made
my signature, sealed me in the book of life.

This name was the one that changed shape
in the mouth of the speaker: added syllables
of love, and littleness and brotherly play
like a plant watered daily
to see its colours change and grow.

Today I hand over that name to you
my foreign language. I hereby adopt you
and give my name to history. I hereby
make myself in your image, oh foreign language,
and declare myself a citizen of your state,
in sickness and in health.

I hereby lay to rest
the many-coloured flower of my birth-name.
I will not hear it again in this life.
I know the price that I must pay
and I will indeed pay it.

Meditation

Here is a safe place away from the noise.
The buzzing has stopped
and I am in the cave of my mind.

It is peaceful here
and the turbulence is of my own making.
I try to choose what comes in, and dismiss

what goes out. Sometimes I succeed,
Sometimes I fail.
At times I line the cave with mirrors

so I can see myself as if from the outside
and the outside as if myself.
Sometimes the cave grows dull,

and I am not at all clear where I am, or if
in fact I am anywhere at all.
On occasions I invite someone in

and we sit together in the half-light,
see how the shadows throw shapes -
how we each read them differently.

The Gold Chain

Episode 1

The gold watch and the diamond ring were wrapped in a handkerchief, and the handkerchief dropped into a wooden snuff box, and the snuff box wrapped in thick brown parcel paper and the parcel paper taped and taped again. It was such a small parcel it could fit into the large pocket of his largest coat, and then over this largest coat he wore a cape that covered him up from top to toe. His job was to take the train from Newcastle to London, and in London to go to a café opposite St. Pancras station, and there would be a young soldier with fair hair flopping over his left eye, wearing army combats, drinking tea at the table in the window.

When he arrived, the soldier was sitting at the table looking vacantly out through the window. He was warming his hands around his cup of tea, holding it without drinking. He stood up and held out his hand. Motek thought for a split second before holding out his own hand, as they do here, hand to hand.

Before sitting down, Motek struggled out of his big cape, and curled his hand around the parcel, warm from sitting in his coat for so long close to his body.

"Tell your father he can be quite confident this will reach his brother" the soldier said. His stare was firm and direct and Miecik longed to believe him. When the waiter came, he ordered a hot chocolate as a reward to himself, for travelling so far, for holding this lozenge of new life in his warm pocket, for handing it over safely. He was free now. He had no more to fear the thieves and pickpockets of London. Let them come, he had nothing now to give of any consequence.

Episode 2

Bronich had lived on the floors of others for more nights than he could remember. He was beginning to run out of people who were brave enough, or foolhardy enough, or who were able to trust a stranger for a night, or had a roof under which to sleep. He had run out of station platforms and park benches, he had run out of lung space for another winter of bronchitis. After all he had done, hiding on the underside of the train all the way to Paris, learning the language within months so he could manage the more casual conversations, studying in this language, struggling, studying, taking the exams, failing, picking himself up again, twice, thrice, losing his eyesight, paying for spectacles, catching pneumonia, becoming a doctor; and then being forbidden to practice, and then shunned, and then being homeless so even if he were, in the aftermath of war, accepted, he would have nowhere to practice. It was as if life were a terrier that gripped him in its maw. He longed for it to let him go.

Now sitting on the bench outside the main city post office, he buried his unshaven face in his hands. *I have finished,* he heard himself say. *There is no more I can do. I have finished.*

When he looked up again, there was a young soldier with fair hair flopping over his left eye, sitting beside him. He looked kindly, and his face was familiar.

"I know you," Bronich said wearily.

"I have come from your brother. I am Krongold's son, you may remember me from Warsaw."

It was as if this was a normal thing, to find someone on a park bench who had known you a whole lifetime ago, when you were another person, another name, another language, another human being away.

"You are Krongold's son," said Bronich. "I knew you when you were so high." He spoke so wearily, Krongold had to lean his head towards him to hear him better.

"You sound so tired."

"How could I not be. I can't remember the last time I slept in a bed."

They sat side by side, Krongold waiting for the right moment.

"I have come from your brother and I have something for you."

Bronich didn't even turn his head as the young man reached under his greatcoat, into his pocket and pulled out a package.

"Here, let me give this to you. Please give me your hand for me to give you this. It is very important I put it into your hand. I promised your brother this."

Wearily Bronich turned to him, as if nothing in the world was worth the effort. Krongold took the older man's hand, turned it over in his and flattened the fingers so his palm was prepared for this incomprehensible new gift. It was a bold thing for a young man to do to a much older one, and Bronich momentarily flinched. Krongold placed the package in the open palm, and closed Bronich's fingers over them.

"This will give you a bed to sleep in," he said.

Episode 3

Bronich sold the gold watch and the diamond ring, and with the proceeds was able to purchase a small apartment in the Bastille area of Paris, with a kitchen, bedroom and sitting room that served as his surgery. He became a much-loved doctor of this Paris suburb, married, brought up his daughter, and lived there until the day of his death sixty years later.

So he and his young nephew were joined together in the small acts that save a life, the links that make a chain, the way we are all joined.

PART FOUR – CONNECTION BETWEEN WORLDS

Letters from the Tigner family archive

These letters were found and translated from the Polish in the Tigner family archive and reproduced with their permission

Bochnia 8/7/1941

My darling Juleczku

"I have more luck than brains". Well said, my boy. Good luck, good luck and more good luck. In today's letter I should talk about and sing the praises of my beloved brother, for you must know that this was to be your birthday letter.
I know that it will arrive late, and I am upset that on this day of July 23rd when the world was a new star, a star which is still twinkling on the horizon, you will be without our congratulations and best wishes. But one has to say, it cannot be helped, it wasn't my doing, but for reasons outside my control.
So first of all I wish you (oh with what warmth and sincerity) that your luck should never, never leave you. I in comparison cannot speak at all of my luck, so I conclude that I have more brains. This I am very proud of, but what of it. It doesn't help me at all. So once more I wish you good luck, and hope to see you very soon.
I want, oh I want everything that's good for you. If only one percent of my wishes came true. The birthday part of my letter is now concluded. And now I turn to the boss about more formal business.
Has your job started yet? Are you making progress? And your staff and clerks – are they giving satisfaction? I hope, or rather we all hope together and

separately, that your letter will give more details of your new life style, your work, the people you've met. Does your friend Ludwik enjoy being in Japan? Seriously, how is it there? I wonder if the two of you are making plans together. I expect so. Your present life is completely unknown to us, but you know ours exactly. So I have neither the wish nor the nerves to return to this subject again. Lately we have had no news from you. Our parents sigh and shake their heads sadly. We do so miss the frequent letters from our Julius, how we do miss them. Still one had to make the best of things as they are.

I have to admit I have become for the moment a boring teacher, making boring boring moral statements.

Well I've finished. I admit I am not gifted and have no ability for writing letters. This one won't even make you smile, which I so hoped for. Once again, I wish you the best and you will congratulate me for so long a letter about nothing at all.

With hug and kisses,
Celina

Bochnia 3/9/1941

Hello Julek,

That letter we waited so long, dreamed about, longed for, has arrived. (I can hardly remember your other letter, it was so long ago!). A party mood started up among us all at once- as if someone had waved a magic wand – and darling Mummy danced with darling Daddy and I danced with them and all the rest of the family joined in. Julek are you 100% happy now? If not, then I really don't know what happiness is. Your lessons, all the fun you have, your trips to the seaside, in short, your whole way of life, seems so different, so strange, so foreign and so wonderful to me. You write that I would envy you hundreds of times but I would envy you millions of times. More than once I've wondered what it would be like if I could be with you (rubbish, nonsense, pipedreams, fairy stories, but a fool can dream) and I've come to the conclusion I would take any fate just to be not here at this time where we are, without being able to move anywhere. Unfortunately nobody asks us what we want any more.
Now I must tell you that in Bochnia you are famous. Everyone knows you because your letters circulate around our 'honoured royal residence.' All we have for you are superlatives – compliments and admiration – and then I am struck down afterwards with sadness, sorrow and depression because I feel I am again in such a growing emptiness. There is actually nothing new here. I have to confirm all the gossip. Of course, of course, a pretty, graceful, nice, charming girl etc. etc. Naturally I've changed from the day of our unforgettable and a hundred times cursed parting

but whether for the better or not you'll have to judge for yourself as soon as you can. I am filling up some of my time now: I help out in the soup kitchen (as a waitress – that seems to be the family trade except that I do it for nothing and without any tips). I help out at the school for poor children, just like a real teacher, and I'm learning American and all the other school subjects. Please write me a few words in your new everyday language. Write clearly so I can make it out. I unfortunately can't say a word in it. And did you take with you from Japan a single letter of the old Japanese alphabet? And what does Japanese language sound like?

A person only comes slowly to his senses. I have only just discovered how truly sweet and loving is our dearest Mummy, and Daddy is such a delightful and clever person. I don't know if you're also clever enough to realise this but I think so. Actually, I've always believed it but have only now seen it with my own eyes. The New Year is approaching again – the third without both of you and away from home. But that's too bad because one must accept everything because if one can't have what one likes then one must like what one has. You know already what my wishes are – above all for us to see each other again soon. I wish you a Happy New Year. I wish that not only for you but for the whole world.

Already I have run out of things to say. I've written a little about everything but about nothing properly. I'm scribbling, scribbling whatever comes to my tongue or rather to my pen. Now I close because Cukus will get cross and they're calling me to the Friday night meal so (as you always write) I must go.

Love, lots of kisses and, once more, all the best things in the world.
Cela

PS Regards and good wishes for the New Year to the friends of yours we do not yet know.

27/10/1941

Dearest Julek

My thoughts turn to you ever more frequently and I admire your sound motto, 'One must be lucky'. But what if one isn't? (Think about it and write me a thorough reply). Yes, yes- not every blind hen will find the corn.
You write that you have a lot of different things, little details and so on, to describe but that you haven't enough time to do so. Is that any way to treat your sister? You just don't go out to meet your friends one night (I swear nobody died from that) and there, you have time! Of course, I'll allow all your new friends and acquaintances to contribute to your letter to me. Their postscripts are quite welcome, especially in your new language.
We've been sniffing for several days. We sniff all day. Have you guessed yet? The cocoa and green coffee which you sent have arrived. Our beloved Daddy keeps saying, 'to smell it, just to be able to smell it' so we dare not drink it because once it's used up that's it, we won't even be able to imagine it any more.
Would you consider sending us a photograph of yourself? If so, then send it. I am very curious to see what this English gentleman looks like. I often imagine our whole family around the table (it doesn't matter any more whether it's Ziebna or Bochnia or any other small town as long as we're all together). Unfortunately, one simply must open one's eyes...

This was the last letter received from Celina. All attempts to discover her fate after that day have been unsuccessful.

150

Bochnia
26/10/ 1941

Dear Julek

For you the past two years have been sheer gain while for me, as for many others, they have been a loss. You know very well how thirsty I am for life, how keen I always am to meet new people and explore the world – and for the time being I am left with reliving my memories. I know – and I've met several new people – that I've certainly matured, but I could have done so under different circumstances. I know that all is not yet lost, that I'm young, healthy and strong but I already yearn for life in the broadest sense and am afraid that it shouldn't elude me, that I should manage to reach for it while I still have enough strength and energy to drink in deep draughts.

Your cousin
Irka

November 1986

Dear Julek,

Receiving your letter, I was really shocked because I am very close to your late parents and we spent a lot of time together. We used to walk and talk, we had plenty of free time because we didn't work.
We used to wear our own clothing as American or so citizen. In Krakow I used to live in Grodska 32 just a few doors of your grandparents. I used to be very friendly with the family specially your grandparents. I used to attend the synagogue, a few doors from my place.
Your parents had South American citizenship and 99% of their papers the Germans disqualified as illegal and the result the Germans sent them to the camps.
I spoke to your parents the previous evening and with a good night, see you in the morning. Unfortunately, no morning any more, they disappeared this night. Till that night we used to live in hope to witness the end of the war.
I think it was about 15th November 1944. By their deportation I lost two charming friends. It was a pleasure to be in their company – always happy, smiling, but they couldn't do more than they did to save their lives. It was a matter of circumstances and luck. Their memory have to help you to continue your and your family's way of life. I am sure you have to be proud to be a member of a most outstanding family in Krakow.

Yours - Jozek Horowitz

REFERENCE

Biography – Jane Spiro

Jane Spiro has published two poetry collections, *is a gateway* and *Playing for Time*, two collections of stories for language learners and a novel *Nothing I Touch Stands Still*. As language educator and Reader in Education at Oxford Brookes University, she has lived and worked in four continents and developed resources widely for the creative teaching of language. In 2010 she won a national teaching award for her contribution to poetry education.

Palewell Press

Palewell Press is an independent publisher handling poetry, fiction and non-fiction with a focus on books that foster Justice, Equality and Sustainability. The Editor can be reached on enquiries@palewellpress.co.uk